Power Maths

Year 3 Practice Book 3C

What did you learn in maths last term?

Draw or write what you enjoyed doing most.

This book belongs to _____ .

My class is _____ .

Pearson

Contents

This looks like a good challenge!

Unit 10 – Fractions (2)   **6**
Equivalent fractions (1)   6
Equivalent fractions (2)   9
Equivalent fractions (3)   12
Comparing fractions   15
Comparing and ordering fractions   18
Adding fractions   21
Subtracting fractions   24
Problem solving – adding and subtracting fractions   27
Problem solving – fractions of measures   30
End of unit check   33

Unit 11 – Time   **35**
Months and years   35
Hours in a day   38
Estimating time   41
Telling time to 5 minutes   44
Telling time to the minute (1)   47
Telling time to the minute (2)   50
Telling time to the minute (3)   53
Finding the duration   56
Comparing duration   59
Finding start and end times   62
Measuring time in seconds   65
End of unit check   68

Unit 12 – Angles and properties of shapes   **71**

Turns and angles   71

Right angles in shapes   74

Comparing angles   77

Drawing accurately   80

Types of line (1)   83

Types of line (2)   86

Recognising and describing 2D shapes   89

Recognising and describing 3D shapes   92

Constructing 3D shapes   95

End of unit check   98

Unit 13 – Mass   **101**

Measuring mass (1)   101

Measuring mass (2)   104

Measuring mass (3)   107

Comparing masses   110

Adding and subtracting masses   113

Problem solving – mass   116

End of unit check   119

Unit 14 Capacity   **121**

Measuring capacity (1)   121

Measuring capacity (2)   124

Measuring capacity (3)   127

Comparing capacities   130

Adding and subtracting capacities   133

Problem solving – capacity   136

End of unit check   139

My power points   141

Let's begin!

How to use this book

Do you remember how to use this **Practice Book**?

Use the **Textbook** first so you can learn how to solve new types of problem.

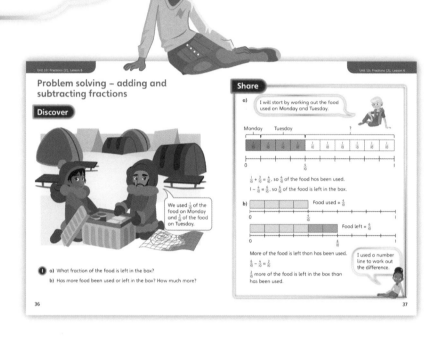

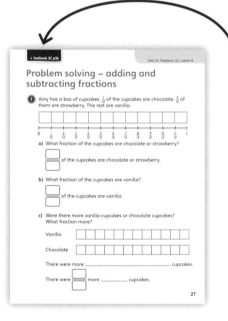

This shows you which **Textbook** page to use.

Have a go at questions by yourself using this **Practice Book**. Use what you have learnt.

Challenge questions make you think hard!

Questions with this light bulb make you think differently.

Reflect

Each lesson ends with a **Reflect** question so you can reflect on what you have learnt.

Use **My power points** at the back of this book to keep track of what you have learnt.

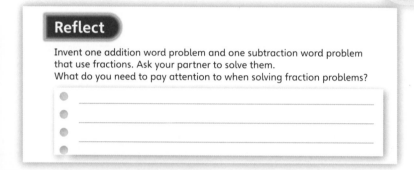

Reflect

Invent one addition word problem and one subtraction word problem that use fractions. Ask your partner to solve them.
What do you need to pay attention to when solving fraction problems?

My journal

At the end of a unit your teacher will ask you to fill in **My journal**.

This will help you show how much you can do now that you have finished the unit.

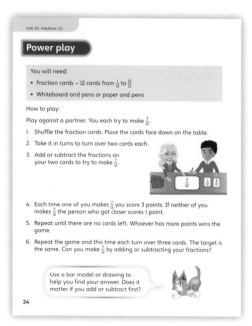

→ Textbook 3C p8

Equivalent fractions

1　Fill in the missing equivalent fractions.

a) $\dfrac{1}{4} = \dfrac{\boxed{}}{8}$

1							
$\frac{1}{4}$		$\frac{1}{4}$		$\frac{1}{4}$		$\frac{1}{4}$	
$\frac{1}{8}$	$\frac{1}{8}$	$\frac{1}{8}$	$\frac{1}{8}$	$\frac{1}{8}$	$\frac{1}{8}$	$\frac{1}{8}$	$\frac{1}{8}$

b) $\dfrac{1}{6} = \dfrac{\boxed{}}{12}$

c) $\dfrac{1}{3} = \dfrac{\boxed{}}{\boxed{}} = \dfrac{\boxed{}}{\boxed{}}$

6

2 Each fraction matches a picture. Draw lines to match them.

$\frac{1}{3}$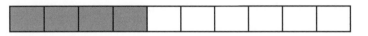

$\frac{2}{5}$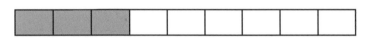

$\frac{1}{4}$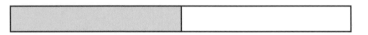

$\frac{1}{2}$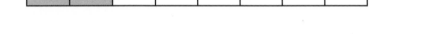

3 Shade the bars to show each fraction. Fill in the equivalent fraction.

a) $\frac{2}{3} = \dfrac{\boxed{}}{9}$

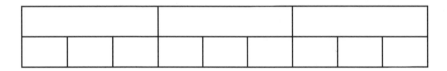

b) $\frac{3}{15} = \dfrac{1}{\boxed{}}$

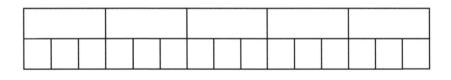

c) $\frac{3}{12} = \dfrac{2}{\boxed{}} = \dfrac{\boxed{}}{\boxed{}}$

4 Shade the fraction in the fraction wall. Then shade its equivalent fractions. Complete the fraction sentence.

$$\frac{6}{8} = \frac{\boxed{}}{\boxed{}} = \frac{\boxed{}}{\boxed{}}$$

5 Olivia has drawn these diagrams. She says that the fractions are equal. Is Olivia correct? Explain your answer.

CHALLENGE

$\frac{2}{5}$

$\frac{1}{3}$

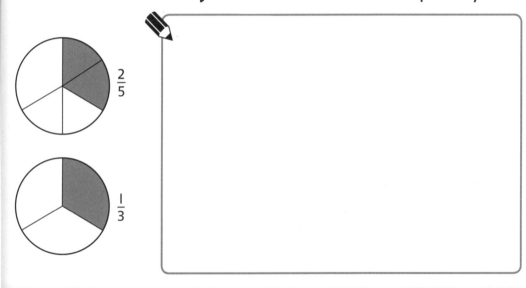

Try drawing a diagram to explain your answer.

Reflect

Explain how you can fold paper to show equivalent fractions.

Equivalent fractions ❷

1 Complete the number lines.

0 $\frac{1}{2}$ $\frac{2}{2}$

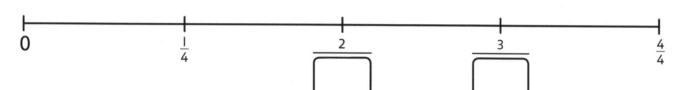

0 $\frac{1}{4}$ $\frac{2}{\square}$ $\frac{3}{\square}$ $\frac{4}{4}$

0 $\frac{1}{5}$ $\frac{2}{\square}$ $\frac{\square}{5}$ $\frac{\square}{\square}$ $\frac{\square}{\square}$

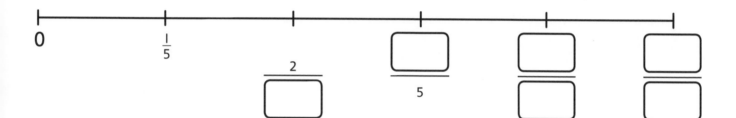

0 $\frac{1}{\square}$ $\frac{\square}{8}$ $\frac{\square}{\square}$ $\frac{\square}{\square}$ $\frac{\square}{\square}$

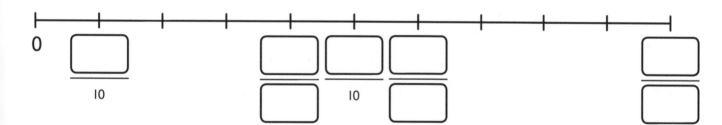

0 $\frac{\square}{10}$ $\frac{\square}{\square}$ $\frac{\square}{10}$ $\frac{\square}{\square}$ $\frac{\square}{\square}$

2 Now use the number lines to work out these equivalent fractions.

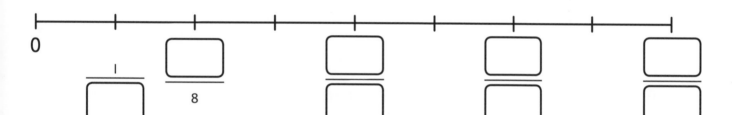

a) $\frac{1}{2} = \frac{\square}{4}$

b) $\frac{1}{2} = \frac{\square}{8}$

c) $\frac{1}{2} = \frac{5}{\square}$

d) $\frac{1}{4} = \frac{\square}{8}$

e) $\frac{1}{5} = \frac{2}{\square}$

f) $\frac{2}{5} = \frac{\square}{10}$

g) $\frac{3}{4} = \frac{6}{\square}$

h) $\frac{3}{5} = \frac{\square}{\square}$

9

3 Complete the equivalent fractions. Use the number lines to help you.

a) $\dfrac{1}{3} = \dfrac{\boxed{}}{6}$ b) $\dfrac{2}{\boxed{}} = \dfrac{4}{6}$ c) $\dfrac{1}{\boxed{}} = \dfrac{3}{\boxed{}}$

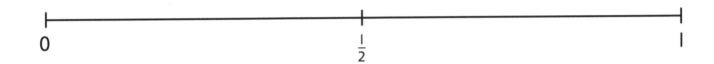

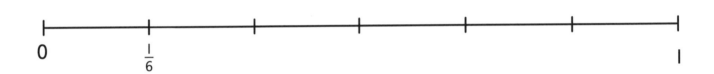

d) Write down three fractions that are not equivalent to $\frac{1}{3}$.

$\dfrac{\boxed{}}{\boxed{}}$ $\dfrac{\boxed{}}{\boxed{}}$ $\dfrac{\boxed{}}{\boxed{}}$

4 Draw arrows to mark these fractions on the number line.

$\frac{1}{2}$ $\frac{1}{4}$ $\frac{3}{4}$

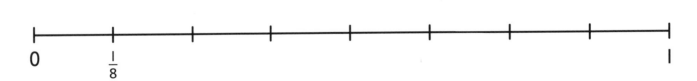

5 Mark $\frac{1}{3}$ on the top number line. Then circle the fractions on the bottom number line that are not equivalent.

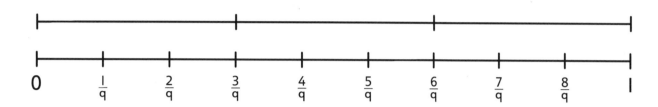

0 $\frac{1}{9}$ $\frac{2}{9}$ $\frac{3}{9}$ $\frac{4}{9}$ $\frac{5}{9}$ $\frac{6}{9}$ $\frac{7}{9}$ $\frac{8}{9}$ 1

6 $\frac{2}{2}$ and $\frac{7}{7}$ are equivalent fractions. How do you know?

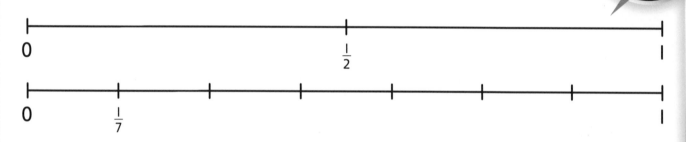

0 $\frac{1}{2}$ 1

0 $\frac{1}{7}$ 1

_____

_____

Can you find two other fractions equal to $\frac{2}{2}$?

Reflect

Explain how to use number lines to find equivalent fractions.

→ Textbook 3C p16

Equivalent fractions ③

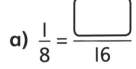

1 Use the bars and number lines to find the missing numerators.

a) $\dfrac{1}{8} = \dfrac{\boxed{}}{16}$

b) $\dfrac{4}{5} = \dfrac{\boxed{}}{10}$

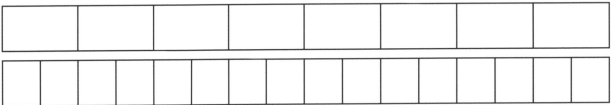

c) $\dfrac{3}{4} = \dfrac{\boxed{}}{12}$

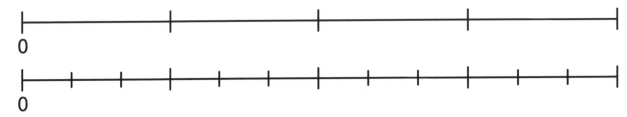

d) $\dfrac{\boxed{}}{4} = \dfrac{12}{16}$

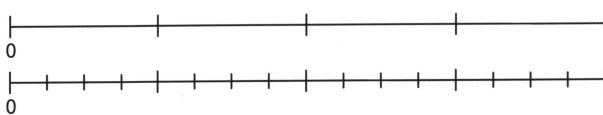

2 **a)** Explain why $\frac{2}{3} = \frac{8}{12}$.

_____

_____

_____

b) Explain why $\frac{2}{5}$ is not equal to $\frac{4}{15}$.

_____

_____

_____

3 Complete the missing numbers. Draw lines to join up any equivalent fractions.

a) $\frac{6}{10} = \dfrac{\boxed{}}{20}$

d) $\dfrac{\boxed{}}{8} = \frac{1}{2}$

g) $\dfrac{\boxed{}}{32} = \frac{1}{8}$

b) $\frac{3}{4} = \dfrac{\boxed{}}{16}$

e) $\frac{5}{11} = \dfrac{30}{\boxed{}}$

h) $\dfrac{\boxed{}}{36} = \frac{3}{9}$

c) $\frac{8}{12} = \dfrac{\boxed{}}{6}$

f) $\dfrac{5}{\boxed{}} = \frac{1}{3}$

i) $\frac{5}{7} = \dfrac{\boxed{}}{28}$

I wonder if I should multiply or divide to find the missing numbers.

4 Complete the calculation.

The △ is a number between 35 and 45.

What pairs of numbers could the ○ and △ be?

$$\frac{3}{4} = \frac{\bigcirc}{\triangle}$$

---

5 Emma thinks that $\frac{1}{2}$ is equivalent to $\frac{2}{3}$.

This is how she worked out her answer.

Do you agree with Emma? Explain how you know.

$$+1$$
$$\frac{1}{2} = \frac{2}{3}$$
$$+1$$

CHALLENGE

_____

_____

_____

Reflect

Explain why $\frac{4}{10}$ is equivalent to $\frac{2}{5}$.

_____

_____

Comparing fractions

1 Use the signs <, > and = to compare these fractions.

a) $\frac{1}{2}$  $\frac{1}{3}$

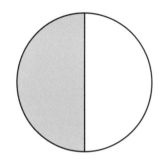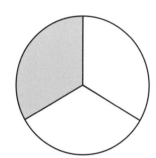

b) $\frac{1}{5}$ ◯ $\frac{1}{6}$

c) $\frac{1}{4}$ ◯ $\frac{4}{16}$

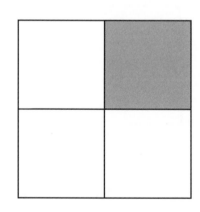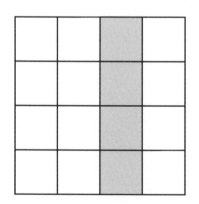

d) $\frac{10}{12}$ ◯ $\frac{9}{10}$

| $\frac{1}{10}$ | $\frac{1}{10}$ | $\frac{1}{10}$ | $\frac{1}{10}$ | $\frac{1}{10}$ | $\frac{1}{10}$ | $\frac{1}{10}$ | $\frac{1}{10}$ | $\frac{1}{10}$ | $\frac{1}{10}$ |

| $\frac{1}{12}$ | $\frac{1}{12}$ | $\frac{1}{12}$ | $\frac{1}{12}$ | $\frac{1}{12}$ | $\frac{1}{12}$ | $\frac{1}{12}$ | $\frac{1}{12}$ | $\frac{1}{12}$ | $\frac{1}{12}$ | $\frac{1}{12}$ | $\frac{1}{12}$ |

2 Shade the bars in the fraction wall to help you compare the fractions.

a) $\frac{1}{8}$ ◯ $\frac{1}{9}$

b) $\frac{5}{6}$ ◯ $\frac{2}{3}$

c) $\frac{2}{5}$ ◯ $\frac{5}{12}$

d) $\frac{3}{4}$ ◯ $\frac{9}{10}$

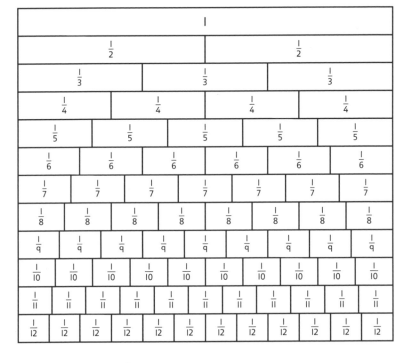

3 Find the missing denominators. Write two answers for each fraction.

a) $\frac{1}{6} < \frac{1}{\boxed{}}$ or $\frac{1}{\boxed{}}$

c) $\frac{1}{\boxed{}}$ or $\frac{1}{\boxed{}} > \frac{1}{8}$

b) $\frac{1}{6} > \frac{1}{\boxed{}}$ or $\frac{1}{\boxed{}}$

d) $\frac{1}{\boxed{}}$ or $\frac{1}{\boxed{}} < \frac{1}{8}$

4 If $\dfrac{\boxed{}}{5} > \dfrac{\boxed{}}{4}$, what numbers could the numerators be?

_____

_____

5 Make two true statements. Choose from 1, 2, 3, 6 and signs < or =.

$\dfrac{\boxed{}}{\boxed{}}$ ◯ $\dfrac{\boxed{}}{\boxed{}}$ $\dfrac{\boxed{}}{\boxed{}}$ ◯ $\dfrac{\boxed{}}{\boxed{}}$

6 Amelia writes down a fraction from the fraction wall.

It is greater than $\frac{1}{2}$ but less than $\frac{3}{4}$.

What is the smallest fraction that Amelia may have written?

What is the greatest fraction that Amelia may have written?

CHALLENGE

1											
$\frac{1}{2}$						$\frac{1}{2}$					
$\frac{1}{3}$				$\frac{1}{3}$				$\frac{1}{3}$			
$\frac{1}{4}$			$\frac{1}{4}$			$\frac{1}{4}$			$\frac{1}{4}$		

(fraction wall down to twelfths)

Reflect

Aki thinks that $\frac{2}{3} < \frac{2}{5}$ because 3 < 5.

What would you tell Aki to explain how to compare fractions?

→ Textbook 3C p24

Comparing and ordering fractions

Use this fraction wall and number line with all the questions in this lesson.

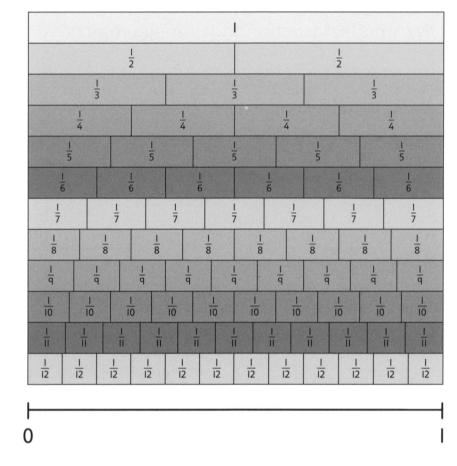

1) What could the missing numbers be? Write one of the possible answers in each box.

a) $\dfrac{6}{12} < \dfrac{\boxed{}}{12}$

b) $\dfrac{3}{10} > \dfrac{\boxed{}}{10}$

c) $\dfrac{\boxed{}}{3} > \dfrac{2}{3}$

d) $\dfrac{5}{8} < \dfrac{6}{\boxed{}}$

e) $\dfrac{2}{3} > \dfrac{2}{\boxed{}}$

f) $\dfrac{7}{\boxed{}} > \dfrac{7}{10}$

g) $\dfrac{1}{2} < \dfrac{\boxed{}}{\boxed{}}$

h) $\dfrac{3}{\boxed{}} > \dfrac{2}{\boxed{}}$

i) $\dfrac{3}{\boxed{}} < \dfrac{2}{\boxed{}}$

18

2 Order the fractions from smallest to largest.

a) $\frac{3}{12}$ $\frac{1}{2}$ $\frac{7}{12}$

b) $\frac{1}{5}$ $\frac{1}{8}$ $\frac{1}{3}$

c) $\frac{4}{8}$ $\frac{4}{6}$ $\frac{4}{10}$

3 The fractions on this number line are in order from the smallest fraction to the largest.

0 ⟶ $\frac{1}{10}$ ⟶ $\frac{1}{2}$ ⟶ $\frac{1}{5}$ ⟶ $\frac{9}{10}$ ⟶ 1

a) Circle the fraction that is in the wrong place.

b) Write it in the correct place.

4 What could Alex's fraction be?
Write three possible answers.

_____

_____

_____

I am thinking of a unit fraction. It is less than $\frac{1}{2}$ but greater than $\frac{1}{6}$.

The numerator of a unit fraction is always 1.

19

5 Ebo writes three fractions on the number line.

The sum of the numerator and denominator in each fraction is 10.

CHALLENGE

What could Ebo's fractions be? Write the fractions in the boxes.

I wonder if there is another fraction Ebo could write on the number line.

Reflect

Complete the sentences.

- I find it easy to compare fractions by _____
- _____
- _____
- I find it tricky when _____
- _____
- _____

Adding fractions

1 Add these fractions. Colour in the shapes to help you.

a) $\dfrac{4}{7} + \dfrac{2}{7} = \dfrac{\Box}{\Box}$

c) $\dfrac{7}{12} + \dfrac{1}{12} = \dfrac{\Box}{\Box}$

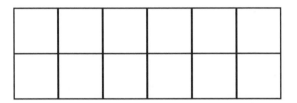

b) $\dfrac{2}{9} + \dfrac{3}{9} = \dfrac{\Box}{\Box}$

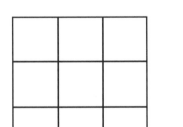

d) $\dfrac{5}{10} + \dfrac{5}{10} = \dfrac{\Box}{\Box}$

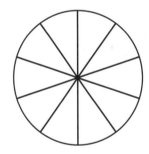

2 Add these fractions. Use the number lines to help you.

a) $\dfrac{3}{5} + \dfrac{1}{5} = \dfrac{\Box}{\Box}$

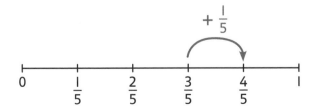

b) $\dfrac{1}{4} + \dfrac{2}{4} = \dfrac{\Box}{\Box}$

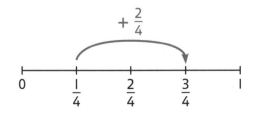

3 Complete the calculations that are shown on the number lines.

a) $\frac{5}{9} + \dfrac{\boxed{}}{\boxed{}} = \dfrac{\boxed{}}{\boxed{}}$

b) $\dfrac{\boxed{}}{\boxed{}} + \dfrac{\boxed{}}{\boxed{}} = \dfrac{\boxed{}}{\boxed{}}$

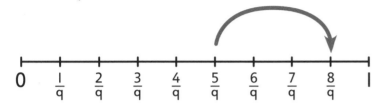
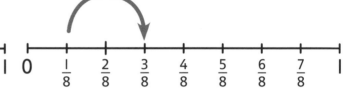

4 Add the fractions.

a) $\frac{1}{3} + \frac{1}{3} = \dfrac{\boxed{}}{\boxed{}}$

b) $\frac{2}{4} + \frac{2}{4} = \dfrac{\boxed{}}{\boxed{}}$

c) $\frac{3}{9} + \frac{2}{9} = \dfrac{\boxed{}}{\boxed{}}$

d) $\dfrac{\boxed{}}{\boxed{}} = \frac{2}{6} + \frac{2}{6}$

e) $\frac{1}{8} + \frac{3}{8} = \dfrac{\boxed{}}{\boxed{}}$

f) $\frac{3}{5} + \frac{1}{5} = \dfrac{\boxed{}}{\boxed{}}$

g) $\frac{3}{10} + \frac{5}{10} = \dfrac{\boxed{}}{\boxed{}}$

h) $\frac{3}{12} + \frac{9}{12} = \dfrac{\boxed{}}{\boxed{}}$

i) $\frac{1}{7} + \frac{1}{7} + \frac{1}{7} = \dfrac{\boxed{}}{\boxed{}}$

5 The sum of two fractions is $\frac{5}{6}$. What could the fractions be?

 a) Which fractions make I when added together?
Draw lines to join the fractions.

$\frac{5}{8}$ 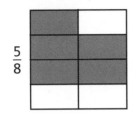 $\frac{3}{4}$ 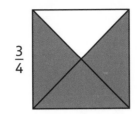 $\frac{3}{8}$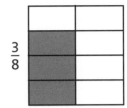

$\frac{1}{2}$ 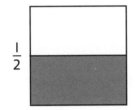 $\frac{1}{4}$ 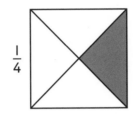 $\frac{1}{2}$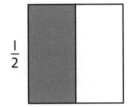

b) Complete the calculations.

$\frac{1}{5} + \frac{\boxed{}}{5} = 1$ 　　 $\frac{3}{6} + \frac{3}{\boxed{}} = 1$ 　　 $\frac{\boxed{}}{10} + \frac{7}{\boxed{}} = 1$

Reflect

Richard thinks that $\frac{1}{5} + \frac{1}{5} = \frac{2}{10}$ because I + I = 2 and 5 + 5 = 10.

Jamilla thinks that $\frac{1}{5} + \frac{1}{5} = \frac{2}{5}$.

Who is correct? Explain how to add fractions with the same denominator.

→ Textbook 3C p32

Subtracting fractions

1 Subtract the fractions. Cross out parts of the diagrams to help you.

a) $\frac{7}{9} - \frac{3}{9} = \frac{\boxed{}}{\boxed{}}$

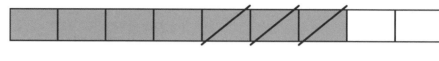

b) $\frac{7}{10} - \frac{5}{10} = \frac{\boxed{}}{\boxed{}}$

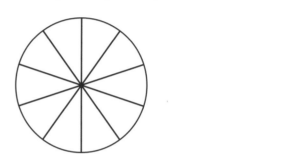

c) $\frac{11}{12} - \frac{5}{12} = \frac{\boxed{}}{\boxed{}}$

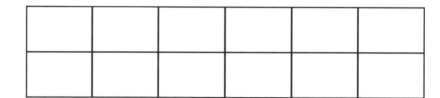

d) $1 - \frac{1}{8} = \frac{\boxed{}}{\boxed{}}$

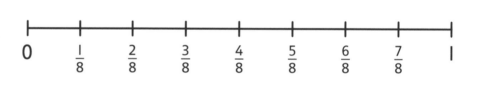

2 Max cuts a cake into 8 slices. He eats 5 slices.

What fraction of the cake does he have left?

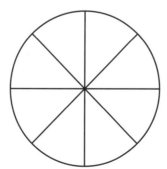

Max has $\frac{\boxed{}}{\boxed{}}$ of the cake left.

24

3 Use the number lines to subtract the fractions.

a) $1 - \frac{1}{3} = \dfrac{\boxed{}}{\boxed{}}$

b) $\frac{7}{8} - \frac{2}{8} = \dfrac{\boxed{}}{\boxed{}}$

c) $\frac{5}{6} - \frac{4}{6} = \dfrac{\boxed{}}{\boxed{}}$

4 Subtract to find the answers.

a) $\frac{5}{9} - \frac{2}{9} = \dfrac{\boxed{}}{\boxed{}}$

d) $\dfrac{\boxed{}}{\boxed{}} = \frac{3}{10} - \frac{1}{10}$

g) $\frac{5}{6} - \dfrac{\boxed{}}{\boxed{}} = \frac{1}{6}$

b) $\frac{3}{8} - \frac{2}{8} = \dfrac{\boxed{}}{\boxed{}}$

e) $\frac{10}{11} - \dfrac{\boxed{}}{11} = \frac{3}{11}$

h) $1 - \dfrac{\boxed{}}{\boxed{}} = \frac{1}{9}$

c) $1 - \frac{3}{4} = \dfrac{\boxed{}}{\boxed{}}$

f) $\frac{7}{8} - \dfrac{2}{\boxed{}} = \frac{5}{8}$

i) $\frac{8}{9} = 1 - \dfrac{\boxed{}}{\boxed{}}$

5 Two fractions have a difference of $\frac{3}{8}$.

Use the number line to find three pairs of fractions that have a difference of $\frac{3}{8}$.

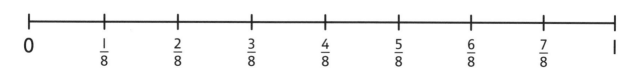

6 Complete the calculation shown on the number line.

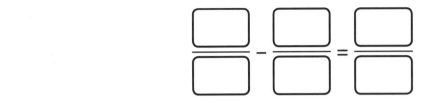

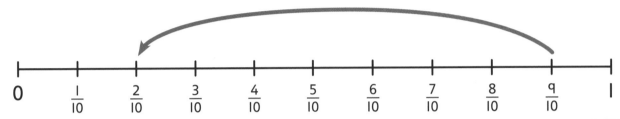

7 Complete the calculations.

CHALLENGE

a) $\dfrac{2}{5} + \dfrac{2}{5} - \dfrac{3}{5} = \dfrac{\Box}{\Box}$

c) $\dfrac{7}{12} - \dfrac{1}{12} + \dfrac{\Box}{\Box} = 1$

b) $\dfrac{5}{9} + \dfrac{\Box}{9} - \dfrac{2}{9} = \dfrac{4}{9}$

d) $1 - \dfrac{\Box}{\Box} + \dfrac{3}{10} = \dfrac{7}{10}$

Reflect

To find the difference between $\dfrac{7}{9}$ and $\dfrac{2}{9}$, Reena calculates $\dfrac{7}{9} - \dfrac{2}{9}$.

Explain how Reena could find the answer.

Problem solving – adding and subtracting fractions

1 Amy has a box of cupcakes. $\frac{1}{12}$ of the cupcakes are chocolate. $\frac{3}{12}$ of them are strawberry. The rest are vanilla.

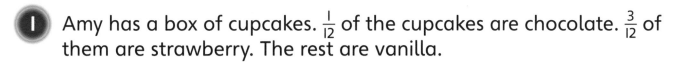

$0 \quad \frac{1}{12} \quad \frac{2}{12} \quad \frac{3}{12} \quad \frac{4}{12} \quad \frac{5}{12} \quad \frac{6}{12} \quad \frac{7}{12} \quad \frac{8}{12} \quad \frac{9}{12} \quad \frac{10}{12} \quad \frac{11}{12} \quad 1$

a) What fraction of the cupcakes are chocolate or strawberry?

 of the cupcakes are chocolate or strawberry.

b) What fraction of the cupcakes are vanilla?

of the cupcakes are vanilla.

c) Were there more vanilla cupcakes or chocolate cupcakes? What fraction more?

Vanilla

Chocolate

There were more _____ cupcakes.

There were more _____ cupcakes.

27

2 Emma is on holiday for 9 days. It snows for $\frac{4}{9}$ of the holiday and is windy for the rest of the holiday.

a) What fraction of the holiday is windy?

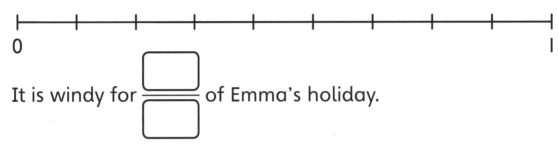

It is windy for $\dfrac{\square}{\square}$ of Emma's holiday.

b) Is it windy for a greater amount of the holiday or is it snowy for a greater amount? How do you know?

It is _____ for a greater amount of the holiday because

_____

_____

3 The answer to a question is $\frac{3}{10}$.

a) What fractions can you add to get the answer $\frac{3}{10}$?

$\dfrac{\square}{\square} + \dfrac{\square}{\square} = \dfrac{3}{10}$ $\dfrac{\square}{\square} + \dfrac{\square}{\square} = \dfrac{3}{10}$

b) What fractions can you subtract to get the answer $\frac{3}{10}$?

$\dfrac{\square}{\square} - \dfrac{\square}{\square} = \dfrac{3}{10}$ $\dfrac{\square}{\square} - \dfrac{\square}{\square} = \dfrac{3}{10}$

c) What fractions can you add, and then subtract, to get the answer $\frac{3}{10}$?

$\dfrac{\square}{\square} + \dfrac{\square}{\square} - \dfrac{\square}{\square} = \dfrac{3}{10}$ $\dfrac{\square}{\square} + \dfrac{\square}{\square} - \dfrac{\square}{\square} = \dfrac{3}{10}$

4 On Monday, Luis read $\frac{1}{10}$ of a book. On Tuesday, he read $\frac{1}{10}$ more than he did on Monday. On Wednesday, he reached halfway. What fraction of the book did Luis read on Wednesday?

Luis read ▢/▢ of the book on Wednesday.

5 Ebo eats $\frac{3}{7}$ of a pizza.

Andy eats $\frac{2}{7}$ less than Ebo.

Ebo says, 'We ate $\frac{5}{7}$ of the pizza in total.'

Is Ebo correct? Explain your answer.

_____

_____

CHALLENGE

How can you check your answer is correct?

Reflect

Invent one addition word problem and one subtraction word problem that use fractions. Ask your partner to solve them.
What do you need to pay attention to when solving fraction problems?

_____

_____

_____

→ **Textbook 3C p40**

Problem solving – fractions of measures

1 Bella has 40 bottles of juice. $\frac{1}{4}$ of the bottles are orange; the rest are apple.

40 bottles

a) What fraction are apple juice?

$\frac{\boxed{}}{\boxed{}}$ of the bottles are apple juice.

b) How many bottles of apple juice are there?

There are $\boxed{}$ bottles of apple juice.

2 Circle the greater amount for each question. Use the fraction strips to help you.

a) $\frac{1}{3}$ of 1 litre of water or $\frac{1}{4}$ of 1 litre of water?

1 litre

1 litre

b) $\frac{2}{6}$ of 20 kg or $\frac{2}{5}$ of 20 kg?

20 kg

20 kg

c) $\frac{1}{5}$ of 10 hours or $\frac{1}{8}$ of 10 hours?

10 hours

10 hours

d) $\frac{3}{9}$ of a 12 cm strip of paper or $\frac{3}{8}$ of a 12 cm strip of paper?

12 cm

12 cm

3 Kate had tennis, netball or swimming every day in April.

Kate played netball on $\frac{3}{10}$ of the days in April. She played tennis on $\frac{1}{10}$ of the days and went swimming on the rest of the days.

a) Did Kate play more netball or tennis?

I will draw a diagram to help work out the answer.

I wonder if I can find the answer without working out the days Kate played tennis or netball.

April						
S	M	T	W	T	F	S
1	2	3	4	5	6	7
8	9	10	11	12	13	14
15	16	17	18	19	20	21
22	23	24	25	26	27	28
29	30					

Kate played more _____ .

b) Kate thinks that she went swimming on more than $\frac{1}{2}$ of the days in April. Is she correct? Explain your answer.

30 days

_____

_____

31

4 Lee and Ambika used 10 m of ribbon to decorate gifts. Lee used $\frac{1}{5}$ of the ribbon. Ambika used $\frac{2}{5}$ more ribbon than Lee.

Was there any ribbon left? Explain your answer.

10 m

_____

_____

_____

5 Mo planted a sunflower that was 12 cm tall, and then measured the plant every week. After the 1st week it had grown $\frac{1}{6}$ of its starting height. After the 2nd week it had grown another $\frac{2}{6}$ of its starting height.

CHALLENGE

How tall was the plant at the end of the second week?

Reflect

Olivia has £10 to buy fruit. She spends $\frac{1}{5}$ on bananas and $\frac{2}{5}$ on cherries. Explain how Olivia can calculate how much she has left.

_____

_____

_____

End of unit check

My journal

What can you say about the circle compared with the square?

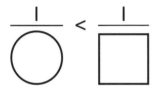

_____

_____

_____

_____

What can you say about the triangle compared with the pentagon?

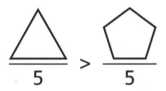

_____

_____

_____

_____

Power check

How do you feel about your work in this unit?

Power play

You will need:

- Fraction cards – 12 cards from $\frac{1}{12}$ to $\frac{12}{12}$

- Whiteboard and pens or paper and pens

How to play:

Play against a partner. You each try to make $\frac{7}{12}$.

1. Shuffle the fraction cards. Place the cards face down on the table.

2. Take it in turns to turn over two cards each.

3. Add or subtract the fractions on your two cards to try to make $\frac{7}{12}$.

4. Each time one of you makes $\frac{7}{12}$ you score 3 points. If neither of you makes $\frac{7}{12}$ the person who got closer scores 1 point.

5. Repeat until there are no cards left. Whoever has more points wins the game.

6. Repeat the game and this time each turn over three cards. The target is the same. Can you make $\frac{7}{12}$ by adding or subtracting your fractions?

Use a bar model or drawing to help you find your answer. Does it matter if you add or subtract first?

Months and years

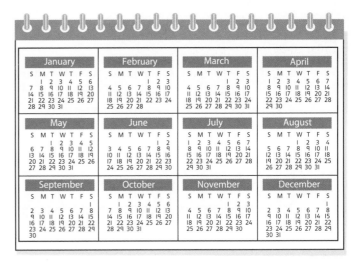

1 Use the calendar to help answer these questions.

a) Start on 20 September. Count forwards one week. What date is it?

_____

b) Start on 1 May. Count backwards 10 days. What date is it?

_____

c) Start on 15 November. Count forwards 14 days. What date is it?

_____

d) Write down a quick way to find these answers.

2 It is 15 January in a leap year.

How many days are left in the year?

There are [   ] days left in the year.

3 Colour the months with 31 days red.

Colour the months with 30 days yellow.

Colour the months with fewer than 30 days blue.

JAN	FEB	MAR	APR	MAY	JUN	JULY	AUG	SEPT	OCT	NOV	DEC

4 Complete the facts with the correct numbers.

$365\frac{1}{4}$ 12   366   365   1

The time it takes for Earth to travel once around the Sun is

☐ year.

Earth takes ☐ days to travel once around the Sun.

Most years have ☐ days.

Leap years have ☐ days.

Every year has ☐ months.

5 Andy says that there are 32 days until the end of the year.

What date is it? _____

How many days of the year have already gone by? ☐ days

6 2000 2001 2002 2003 2004 2005 2006 2007 2008

⬤ Common year ◯ Leap year

Leap years usually occur once every four years.
The year 2000 was a leap year.

Look carefully at the number of each leap year.

Without counting every year, circle the years that will be leap years.

2021   2034   2036   2042   2044

Will the year 2045 be a leap year?   Yes / No

How do you know?

_____

_____

_____

CHALLENGE

Reflect

Gemma says that in 2016 there were 90 days altogether in January, February and March.

Is this true? Was it true for 2017?

Explain your answer.

_____

_____

_____

→ Textbook 3C p52

Hours in a day

1 Draw the times and label each clock to show 24 hours later.

I o'clock Wednesday

24 hours later

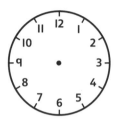

_____

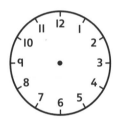

_____

24 hours later

5 o'clock Saturday

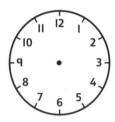

_____

24 hours later

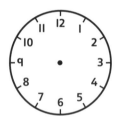

_____

2 Write each letter in the correct circle.

A: a whole day

B: from 12 midnight until 12 noon

C: half a day

D: from 2 o'clock in the afternoon one day until 2 o'clock in the afternoon the next day

E: the length of time that Monday takes

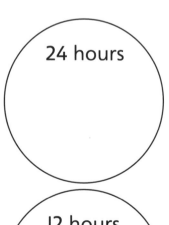

24 hours

12 hours

3 Complete the bar diagrams to show how many hours are in each length of time.

24 hours

I day = 24 hours

24 hours	24 hours

☐ days = ☐ hours

24 hours	☐ hours	☐ hours

☐ days = ☐ hours

☐ hours	☐ hours	☐ hours	☐ hours	☐ hours	☐ hours	☐ hours

I week = ☐ days = ☐ hours

4 Colour each grid to show the number of hours in each fraction of a day.

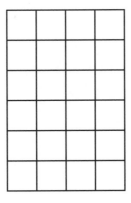

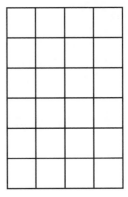

$\frac{1}{2}$ of a day =

☐ hours

$\frac{1}{4}$ of a day =

☐ hours

$\frac{1}{3}$ of a day =

☐ hours

5 Aki is being sponsored for a 24-hour silence.

He starts at 8 o'clock in the evening.

a) It is 6 o'clock in the evening on the next day. How long has Aki been silent? ⬚ hours

b) How long has Aki got left? ⬚ hours

6 How do you spend a normal day?

CHALLENGE

Colour this strip to show the amount of time you spend doing things such as sleeping, eating, learning and playing.

I block is I hour of the day.

Draw a key to show what each colour represents.

Reflect

Olivia thinks a day begins when she gets up, and ends when she goes to bed.

Explain to her how long a day really is.

Estimating time

1 Draw the hour hand on each clock face.

a)

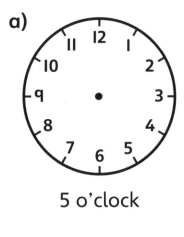

5 o'clock

c)

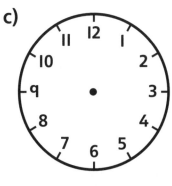

quarter past 9

b)

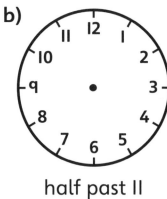

half past 11

d)

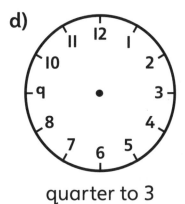

quarter to 3

2 Draw where you estimate the minute hand will be on each clock. Write the time underneath.

_____   _____   _____

3 The hour hand on a clock face is more than half-way between 11 and 12. Tick the times that it could be.

quarter to 12 ☐   quarter past 12 ☐   ten past 11 ☐

twenty-five to 12 ☐   half past 11 ☐   five to 12 ☐

4 Emma can only see half a clock face. She says, 'I can only see the hour hand, so I cannot estimate the time.' Is Emma right? Explain.

_____

_____

_____

_____

_____

5 Work out how many minutes are shown on each clock by the movement of the hour hand. Use the fractions below each clock to help. Remember, there are 60 minutes in 1 hour.

a)   b)   c)   d)

$\frac{1}{2}$ of 1 hour = $\frac{1}{4}$ of 1 hour = $\frac{3}{4}$ of 1 hour = $\frac{1}{5}$ of 1 hour =

☐ minutes   ☐ minutes   ☐ minutes   ☐ minutes

6 Lee can only see the bottom half of a clock face. Both the hands are hidden.

He knows that the time is between 2 and 3 o'clock. What times could it be?

CHALLENGE

_____

_____

_____

Reflect

Complete these sentences using what you have learnt during the lesson.

If I know that the hour hand is half-way between two numbers,

I know that _____

_____

If I know that the hour hand is between the 5 and the 6,

I know that _____

_____

If I know that the hour hand is between the 2 and the 3, but is

nearer to the 2, I know that _____

_____

_____

→ Textbook 3C p60

Telling time to 5 minutes

1 What times do these clocks show?

First, I will look at how far the minute hand has moved past an o'clock time.

Remember to count in 5s!

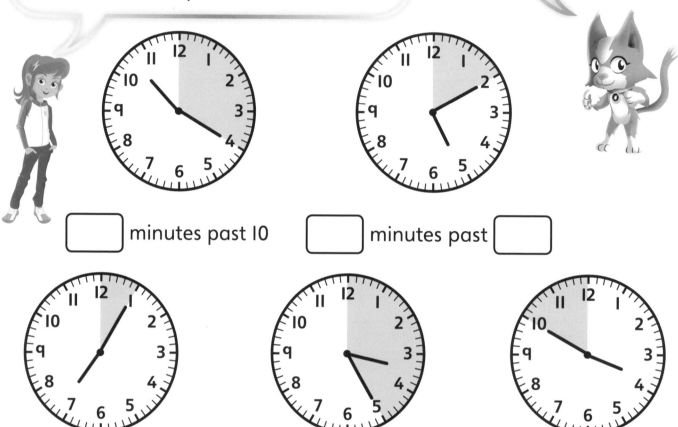

[ ] minutes past 10   [ ] minutes past [ ]

[ ] minutes past [ ]   [ ] minutes past [ ]   [ ] minutes past [ ]

[ ] minutes to [ ]   [ ] minutes to [ ]   [ ] minutes to [ ]

2 Draw the times on each station clock.

a)

quarter to 11

c)

twenty minutes to 3

b)

twenty-five past 10

d)

ten minutes past 6

3

I think the time is ten past 11.

Explain Lexi's mistake.

_____

_____

_____

_____

4 The minute hand on a station clock is pointing to the 4.

The hour hand is pointing between the 6 and the 7.

What time is it?_____

5 The minute hand is pointing to a number that is more than 7.

The hour hand is between two numbers that add up to 7.

CHALLENGE

a) What could the time be? Explain your answer.

_____

_____

_____

b) Make up your own clues for your partner to work out a time you have chosen.

_____

_____

_____

Reflect

How do you know what the time is? Explain to a partner, using these words:

minute hand, o'clock, hour hand, because

_____

_____

_____

Telling time to the minute ❶

1 Draw the times.

I am leaving for trumpet practice at nine minutes past 4.

This television programme ends at eighteen minutes to 6.

The next bus arrives at twenty-four minutes past 9.

My Gran rang at seven minutes to 11 exactly!

2 Draw each time on the clock face.

a)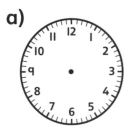
13 minutes past 1

b)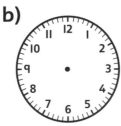
twenty to 9

c)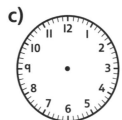
twelve minutes to 8

d)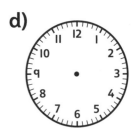
27 minutes past 5

3 Look at the clocks showing 'minutes past'. Match each one with the clock showing the same 'minutes to'. The first pair has been done for you. Write the time beside each clock.

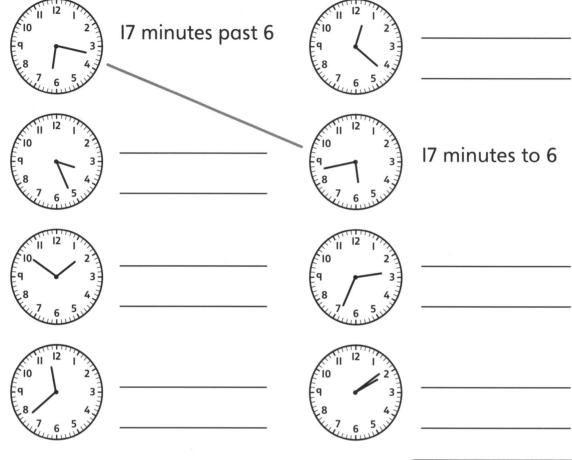

17 minutes past 6

_____

_____

17 minutes to 6

_____

_____

_____

_____

_____

_____

4 What is Kate's mistake?

Explain what she has done and why you think she may have done this.

I think the clock is showing 5 minutes to 2.

_____

_____

_____

5 The time is four minutes past 9.

Gemma needs to check on her cake in the oven every 8 minutes until 10 o'clock.

How many times will she check on her cake?

Write or draw the different times she will need to check on her cake.

CHALLENGE

Reflect

Look at the watch. What have you learnt in today's lesson that helps you to know what time it is?

Today I have learnt that

→ Textbook 3C p68

Telling time to the minute ②

1 Draw each time on the analogue clock. Think carefully!

a) 8:30 pm   **b)** 1:15 am   **c)** 4:45 am   **d)** 10:07 pm

 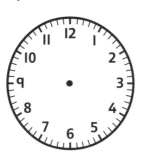 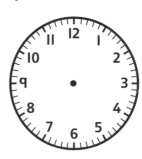 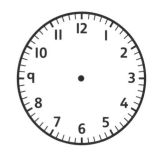

2 Write each time on the digital clock.

a)   **b)**   **c)**   **d)**

   :   :   :   :

3 Write the correct time on each clock. Remember to include 'am' or 'pm'.

a) quarter past 6 in the evening   :   _____

b) half past 7 in the morning   :   _____

c) 9 minutes past 4 in the afternoon   :   _____

d) twenty to 10 in the morning   :   _____

e) 1 minute past midnight   :   _____

4 How would you write this as a digital time?

Show two different possibilities.

5 Draw the hands on the clocks for the times shown.

a)

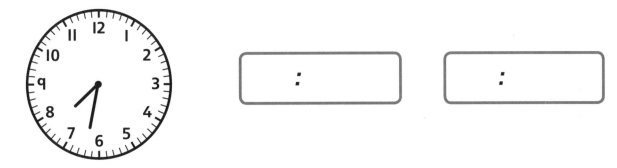

b) What do you notice about the clocks?

_____

_____

6 At 3:45 am the digits on a digital clock are consecutive (they go up by 1 each time).

At which other times in the day will a clock show consecutive digits?

_____

_____

_____

7 Amelia says, 'If I add the digits I can see on my digital clock, the total is 10.' What different times could be on Amelia's clock?

Draw one time on each of the two clocks. Then write the other times.

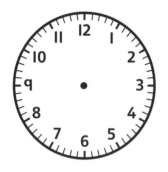

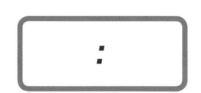

_____

_____

_____

_____

Reflect

Max wakes up and looks out of the window.

It is dark outside.

Explain how it can be an 'am' time if it is night.

_____

_____

Telling time to the minute ❸

1 Draw these 24-hour times on the clocks.

a) 15:30

c) 08:25

e) 21:37

b) 06:12

d) 13:46

f) 01:15

2 Write these times as 24-hour clock times.

a) 4:52 am [:]

3:52 am [:]

2:52 am [:]

1:52 am [:]

12:52 am [:]

b) 5:09 pm [:]

6:09 pm [:]

7:09 pm [:]

8:09 pm [:]

9:09 pm [:]

3

My clock says that the time is 20:00.

But there is no such time as 20 o'clock!

Explain what the time 20:00 means.

_____

_____

_____

_____

4 Draw these times on the clock faces.

a) 17:12

b) 23:40

5 I am a 24-hour clock time between 7 pm and 8 pm.

The total of my four digits is a multiple of 5.

What times could I be?

6 Using only the digits 0, 1, 2, 3 and 4, make ten different 24-hour times.

Convert each time to a 12-hour clock time. State whether each time is am or pm.

CHALLENGE

Remember, if a time is written with only three digits, you will need to use the zero at the start to make four digits.

Which time is latest? ___:___

Which time is earliest? ___:___

Reflect

A clock shows 18:58. Is it the morning or the evening?

Explain how you know.

→ Textbook 3C p76

Finding the duration

Use two jumps if it crosses an o'clock time: one to get to the nearest hour and one to jump beyond it.

1 Shade the clocks to find each duration.

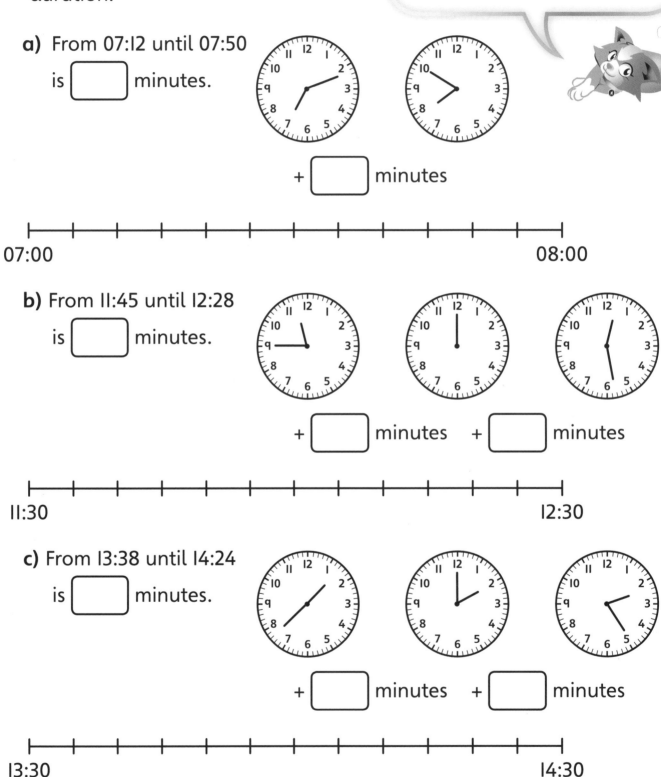

a) From 07:12 until 07:50

is ☐ minutes.

+ ☐ minutes

07:00   08:00

b) From 11:45 until 12:28

is ☐ minutes.

+ ☐ minutes   + ☐ minutes

11:30   12:30

c) From 13:38 until 14:24

is ☐ minutes.

+ ☐ minutes   + ☐ minutes

13:30   14:30

2 **a)** Complete the table to show how long it takes a farmer to do each job.

Job	Start time	End time	Duration
Feeding the pigs	07:35	07:56	
Cleaning out the stables	08:35	09:06	
Mending a fence	09:35	10:16	
Collecting the eggs	10:35	11:26	

b) What do you notice about your answers? Why is this?

_____

_____

3 A milk tanker arrives at a farm at quarter to 6 in the morning.

It fills up with milk and leaves the farm at sixteen minutes past 7. How long does it take the tanker to fill up with milk?

The tanker takes ☐ minutes to fill up with milk.

4 Max thinks that the amount of time between 15:22 and 16:57 is 35 minutes because 57 − 22 = 35.

Is this true or false? _____

Explain your answer. _____

_____

Start time   End time

5 What is the duration between these times?

_____

6 Mr Lopez takes a lunch break of 52 minutes.

He starts lunch at a time after 13:00. He ends it at a time before 14:00.

When could his lunch start and end?

CHALLENGE

I am going to try to find all the possible answers.

Reflect

Write your own duration problem for a partner to answer.

Think about how you want your partner to answer the question.

_____
_____
_____
_____

Comparing duration

1 Alex practises the piano on Mondays and Saturdays.

Shade the clocks to work out how long she spends practising.

a) Monday, from 18:09 until 18:35. Alex spends ☐ minutes.

+ ☐ minutes

b) Saturday, from 18:52 until 19:17. Alex spends ☐ minutes.

+ ☐ minutes

Alex practises for the longer time on _____ .

2 A car park charges £1 for up to 65 minutes.

It charges £3 for more than 65 minutes.

Lee's dad stays in the car park from 10:35 until 11:38.

How much should he pay and why?

3

Bus	Leaves village	Arrives town
A	09:36	10:23
B	09:46	10:27
C	10:42	11:12
D	10:52	11:25

I do not need to calculate the durations to see which bus is quicker.

a) Which bus is quicker, A or B? How do you know?

_____

_____

_____

b) Which bus is quicker, C or D? How do you know?

_____

_____

_____

4 Which is longer, I hour 9 minutes or 63 minutes?

63 minutes is longer than I hour 9 minutes, because 63 is a larger number than I and 9.

I do not think that is a good way to compare.

_____

CHALLENGE

5 There are 110 minutes left before home time.

What combinations of activities could Year 3 do?

Is there a combination of activities that would fill the time exactly?

Activity	Duration
Spelling test	15 minutes
PE	1 hour 5 minutes
Rock & roll maths	20 minutes
Science experiment	1 hour
School library visit	35 minutes

Reflect

The adventure film starts at 15:15 and ends at 17:00. The space film starts at 15:25 and ends at 17:05.

Explain how you know which film is longer.

_____

_____

_____

→ Textbook 3C p84

Finding start and end times

1 It is 1:13 pm and the queue to get into the fair lasts 25 minutes.

If you start queuing now, what time will you get into the fair?

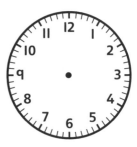

+ 25 =

Start time   Duration   End time

I will get into the fair at _____ .

2 Complete the clocks to show the start and end times.

a)

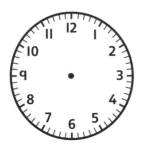

Duration
19 minutes

Start time
2:32 pm

End time
_____

b)

Duration
49 minutes

Start time
_____

End time
3:52 pm

3 The end time of a roller coaster ride is two minutes past 3.

The duration of the ride is 9 minutes.

What was the start time of the ride? _____

Explain how you worked out the answer.

_____

_____

_____

4 Complete the table.

	Start time	Queue length (duration)	End time
Bouncy castle	1:16 pm	22 minutes	
Big dipper		25 minutes	2:37 pm
Go karts	3:48 pm	26 minutes	
Runaway train		24 minutes	5:06 pm

5  Print your own poster in 60 minutes!

 60 plus 5 equals 65. My poster will be ready at 65 minutes past 4.

What has Mo done wrong? When will his poster be ready?

_____

_____

_____

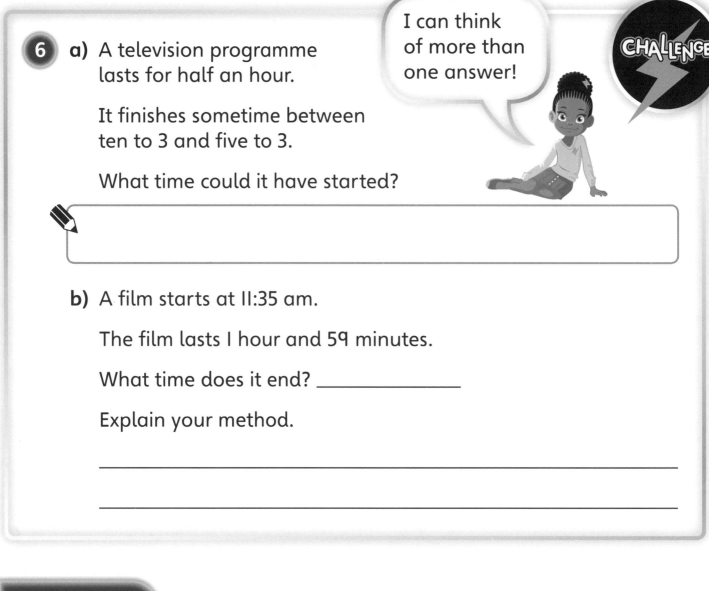

6 **a)** A television programme lasts for half an hour.

It finishes sometime between ten to 3 and five to 3.

What time could it have started?

I can think of more than one answer!

CHALLENGE

b) A film starts at 11:35 am.

The film lasts 1 hour and 59 minutes.

What time does it end? _____

Explain your method.

_____

_____

Reflect

Amelia's piano lesson starts at 6:45 pm and lasts for 55 minutes.

Explain how you would find out what time her lesson ends. Did you do the same as your partner?

Measuring time in seconds

1 Match each clock with the number of seconds that it shows.

a)

b)

c)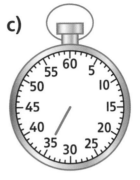

d)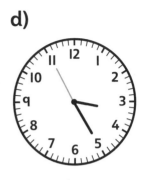

(55 seconds) (40 seconds) (45 seconds) (35 seconds)

2 Complete the table.

Activity	Time in minutes	Time in seconds
Bouncing a ball	$\frac{1}{2}$ a minute	
Running on the spot		120 seconds
Skipping	$1\frac{1}{2}$ minutes	
Star jumps		60 seconds

3 Ebo is timing how long it takes for him to run around the playground.

He starts on 13 seconds.

How long does it take Ebo?

Start time

End time

It takes Ebo [ ] seconds.

4

Jamie

Max

On my stopwatch, there are 43 seconds left until 1 minute has passed.

I have 24 seconds to go!

How many seconds does each stopwatch show? Explain your answers.

_____

_____

_____

_____

_____

5 Ask your partner to start timing in seconds.

Tell your partner when you estimate that 1 minute is up.

Try several different methods for estimating. For example, you could clap 60 times or say, 'I elephant, 2 elephants …, 60 elephants.'

Which method works best for estimating seconds?

_____

_____

_____

_____

_____

_____

CHALLENGE

Reflect

I am going to estimate a minute by counting to 60 as quickly as I can!

What is Bella's mistake?

Explain what she should do differently.

_____

_____

_____

→ Textbook 3C p92

End of unit check

My journal

1 Complete each time and explain how you know what it is.

a)

I know that the time is _____

because _____

_____

b)

I know that the time is _____

because _____

_____

c)

I know that the time is _____

because _____

_____

2 Draw five different things you did yesterday.

Label each one with the time on a clock and in words.

Write your times in different ways (24 hour clock, or using am and pm).

Power check

How do you feel about your work in this unit?

Power play

Start in the top left-hand corner.

If you are playing with a partner, see who can finish more quickly.

You may only move to a time 23 minutes later than the time you are on.

Draw arrows to show your path and circle where you land.

What time do you end on?

12:02 pm	13:11		6:33 pm	18:10	17:47
	12:48 pm	13:57		19:19	
12:58	1:21 pm	2:20 pm		4:38 pm	17:01
13:31	3:16 pm		15:52	16:05	18:10
1:45 pm		15:06	3:29 pm	5:24 pm	

Turns and angles

1 **a)** Max faces the exit.

He turns a right angle clockwise.

Now he faces the _____ .

b) Then he turns two right angles anticlockwise.

Now he faces the _____ .

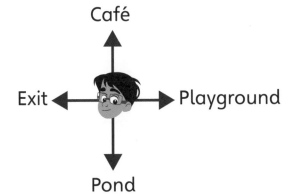

2 Tick all the diagrams that show just one right-angle turn.

☐ ☐ ☐ ☐

☐ ☐ ☐ ☐

3 Face the front of your classroom. Describe what you would be facing if you made:

a) a right-angle turn clockwise: _____

b) three right-angle turns anticlockwise: _____

What do you notice? _____

4 Look at the diagram.

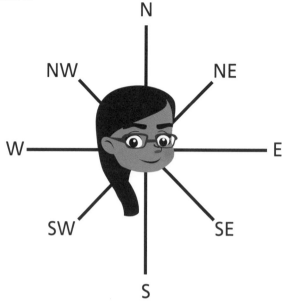

a) Reena faces east (E). She turns two right angles. Where is she facing now?

She is facing _____ .

b) She faces S and turns by a right angle. Where could she be facing?

She could be facing _____ or _____ .

c) Reena is facing a different direction and she turns three right angles clockwise. Now she is facing SE. Where was she facing to begin with? _____

d) Reena is facing NW. Describe the turn she needs to make to face SW. Describe all the different ways.

_____

_____

_____

_____

_____

5 Complete the grid.

CHALLENGE

Starting position	Quarter turn clockwise	Two right-angle turns anticlockwise	Quarter turn anticlockwise	Three-quarter turn anticlockwise then a quarter turn clockwise
↗	↘	↙		
☺				
	♡			
				✚
			⊤	

Reflect

When I turn by two right angles, I will _____

_____

When I turn by four right angles, I will _____

_____

→ **Textbook 3C p100**

Right angles in shapes

1 There are twenty right angles in this football pitch. Can you find and mark all of them? Two have been done for you.

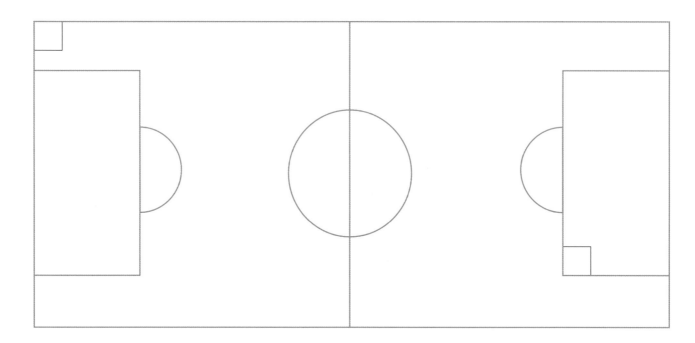

2 Mark all the right angles in these shapes.

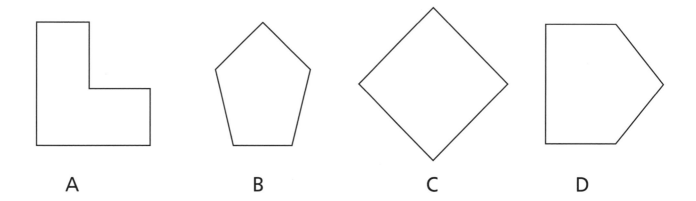

A   B   C   D

3 Circle the places that have been incorrectly marked as right angles.

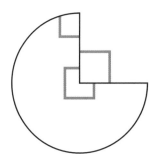 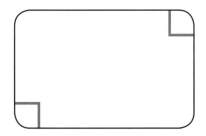 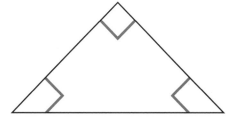

4 Draw perpendicular lines joining the dots to make at least one right angle in each diagram.

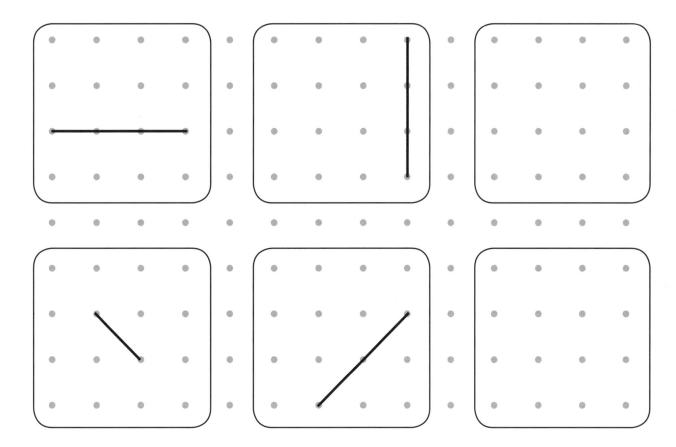

⑤ Describe where you can find right angles in four different places in your classroom.

1	3
2	4

⑥ Use the clues to colour in Ambika's shape.

Ambika's shape is not above the shape with just one right angle.

Ambika's shape is not below a shape with no right angles.

Ambika's shape has at least two right angles.

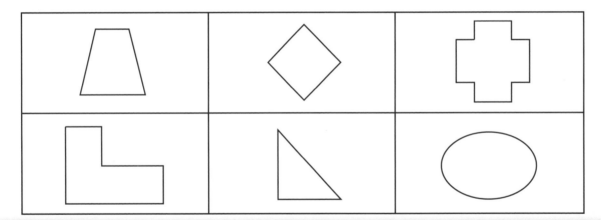

Reflect

Draw a shape with three right angles.

Comparing angles

1 Join each angle with the correct description.

 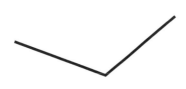 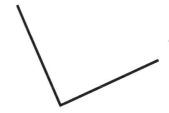

| Greater than a right angle | A right angle | Less than a right angle |

2 Draw three different angles that are less than a right angle and three different angles that are greater than a right angle. Use a ruler.

Less than a right angle (acute)		
Greater than a right angle (obtuse)		

3 Write **acute** or **obtuse** for each angle.

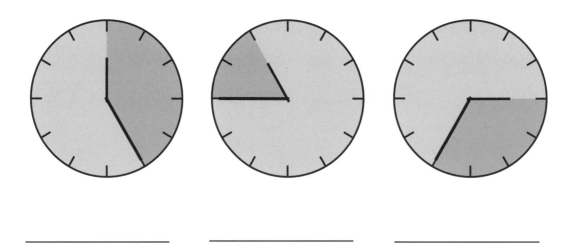

_____   _____   _____

4 Draw three different acute, obtuse and right angles.

acute angles

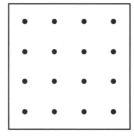 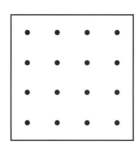 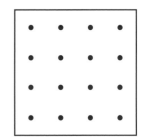

obtuse angles

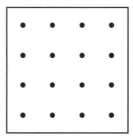 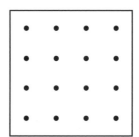 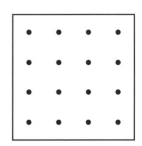

right angles

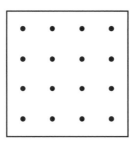 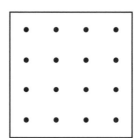 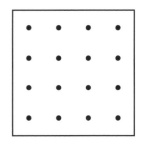

5 Predict which type of angle is most common in this picture. Then check your prediction and write the number of each type of angle.

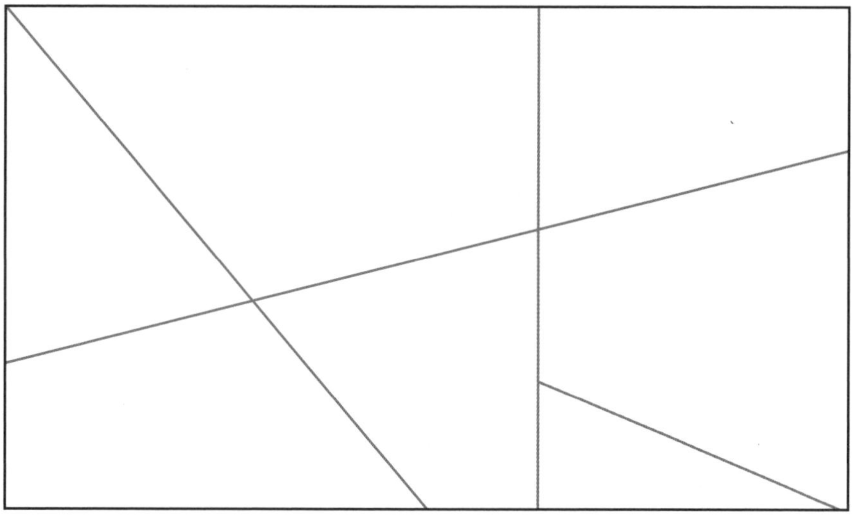

CHALLENGE

_____

_____

[ ] acute angles   [ ] right angles   [ ] obtuse angles

Reflect

Where can you find acute and obtuse angles in school? How can you tell which angles are obtuse and which are acute?

● _____

● _____

● _____

● _____

→ Textbook 3C p108

Drawing accurately

1 Measure each line and draw a copy of each accurately.

A   B   C

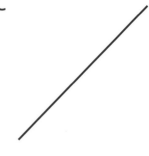

A	B	C

2 Draw lines to split this box into three squares, each 5 cm wide.

3 **a)** Measure the sides of these shapes. Then copy the shapes below as accurately as you can.

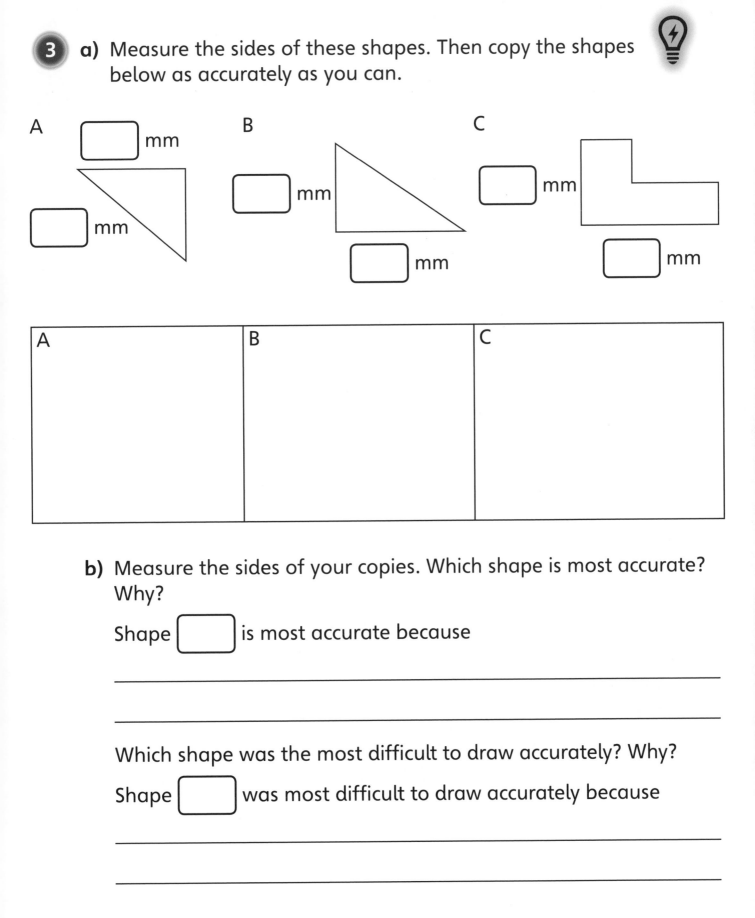

A [   ] mm

[   ] mm

B [   ] mm

[   ] mm

C [   ] mm

[   ] mm

A	B	C

b) Measure the sides of your copies. Which shape is most accurate? Why?

Shape [   ] is most accurate because

_____

_____

Which shape was the most difficult to draw accurately? Why?

Shape [   ] was most difficult to draw accurately because

_____

_____

CHALLENGE

4 Split this square into:

a) A rectangle that is twice as long as it is wide.

b) A square that is half as wide as the large square.

c) Two triangles.

Show the correct measurements of each shape.

Reflect

Explain how to draw a 5 cm 5 mm line accurately.

Step 1 _____

Step 2 _____

Step 3 _____

Types of line ❶

1 Write **horizontal**, **vertical** or **neither** under each line.

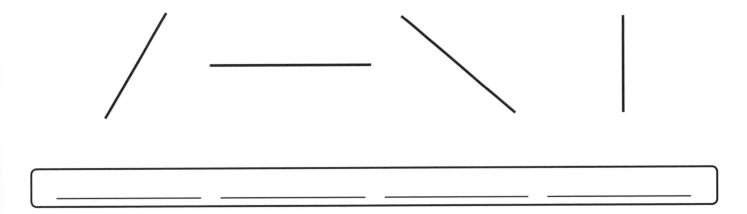

2 Count the number of horizontal lines and vertical lines in this picture. Treat the road level of the bridge as just one line.

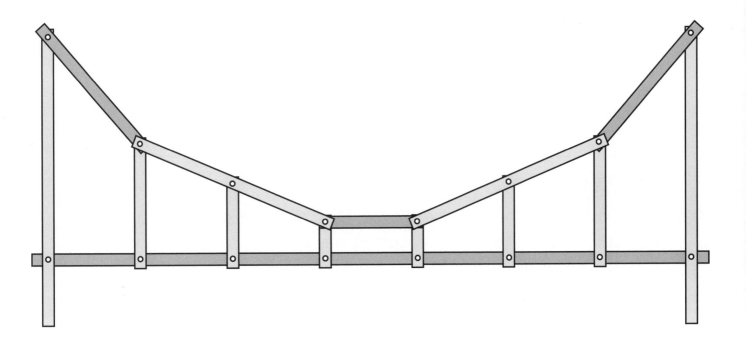

There are ☐ horizontal lines and ☐ vertical lines.

3 Draw three horizontal lines in box A. Draw three vertical lines in box B. Draw three lines that are neither horizontal nor vertical in box C.

A	B	C

4 Draw horizontal and vertical lines of symmetry where they belong on these shapes.

5 Look at the shapes in question 4. Describe the angle of turn needed to change the symmetry lines from vertical to horizontal or horizontal to vertical.

_____

_____

_____

6 Tick the horizontal and vertical lines on this patterned wallpaper. Use a ruler to help you.

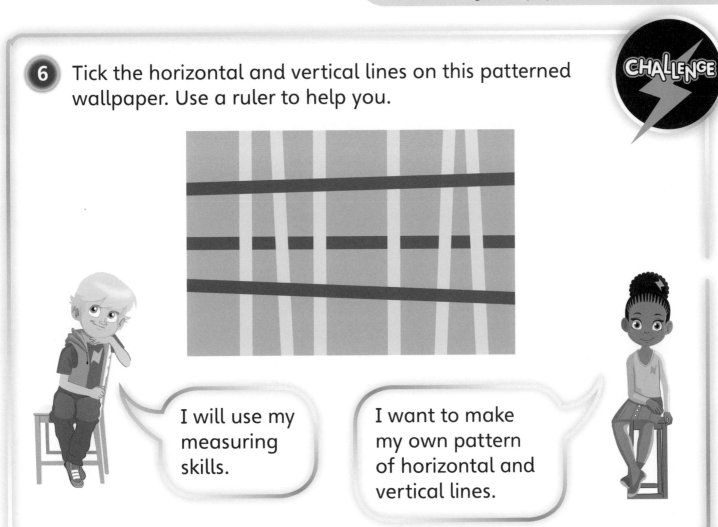

CHALLENGE

I will use my measuring skills.

I want to make my own pattern of horizontal and vertical lines.

Reflect

Explain where you could see something horizontal and something vertical outside of the classroom.

Types of line ❷

a) Tick the pairs of parallel lines. Draw a right-angle marker to show the pair of perpendicular lines.

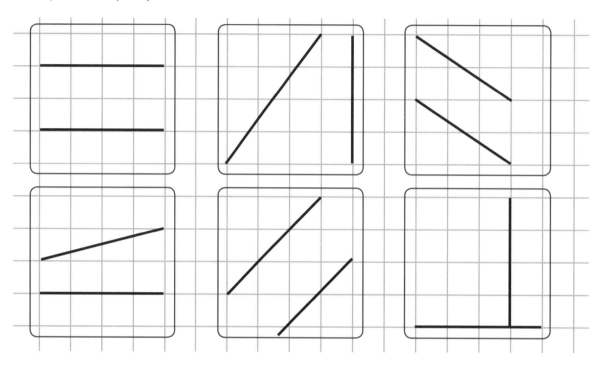

b) Draw lines to make a pair of parallel lines in each box. Make the lines different lengths but still parallel.

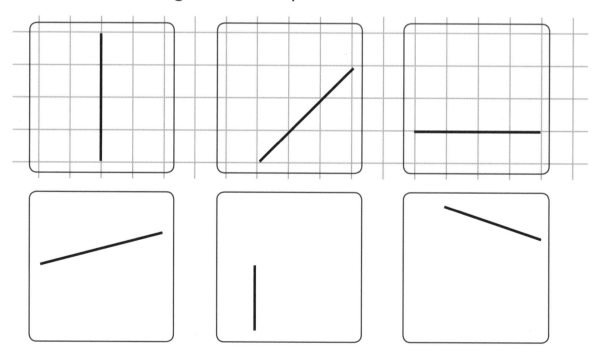

2 Draw and label an example of parallel lines and an example of perpendicular lines.

3 Describe where you might find parallel and perpendicular lines in real life. You can use diagrams to explain your ideas.

_____

_____

_____

_____

4 Is Dexter right or wrong? Explain your answer.

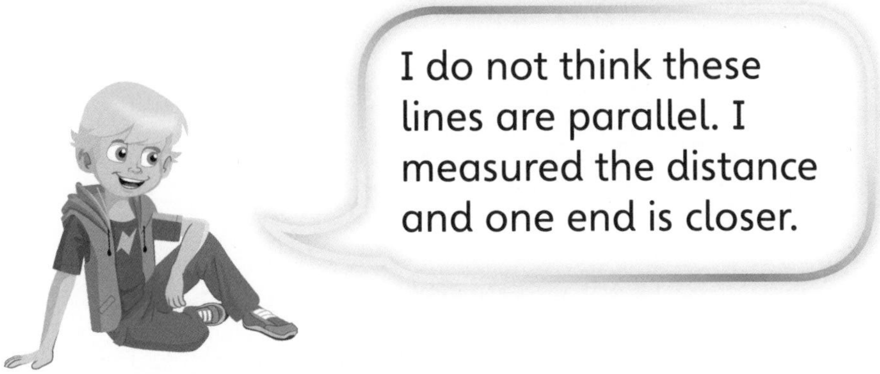

> I do not think these lines are parallel. I measured the distance and one end is closer.

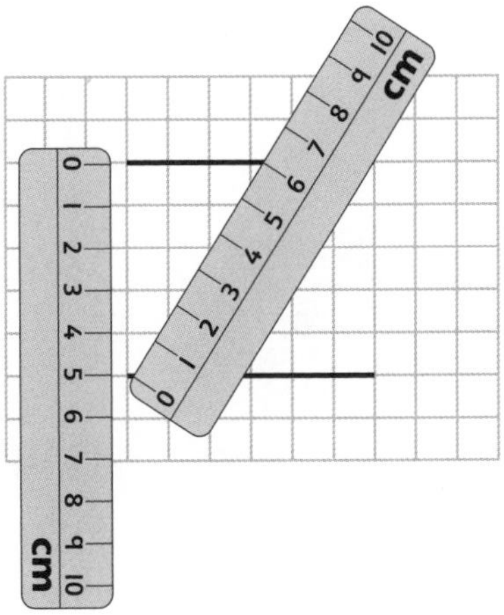

_____

_____

_____

5 **a)** Join dots to make parallel lines in each circle.

CHALLENGE

b) Join dots to make a pair of perpendicular lines in each circle. Use different colours for each pair of lines.

Reflect

What are the most important things people need to know about parallel lines and perpendicular lines?

1. _____

2. _____

3. _____

Recognising and describing 2D shapes

1 Write rectangle, pentagon, hexagon or triangle below the right shape.

  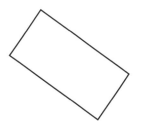 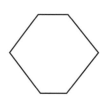

_____ _____ _____ _____

2 Which shape is not a quadrilateral? Explain how you know.

  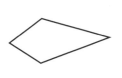

A   B   C   D   E

_____

_____

3 Draw lines of symmetry on these shapes.

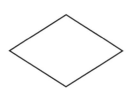  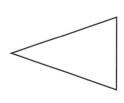 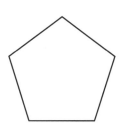

A   B   C   D   E

89

4 Draw two different shapes to match each description.
Write the names of any shapes you recognise.

a) These shapes have two horizontal lines and two vertical lines.

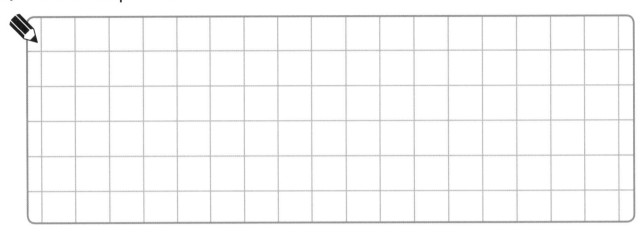

b) These shapes have one pair of perpendicular lines, but no parallel lines.

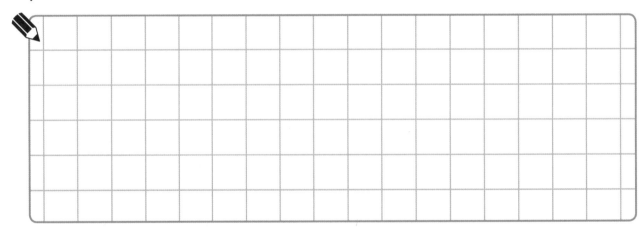

c) These shapes have no parallel or perpendicular lines and one line of horizontal symmetry.

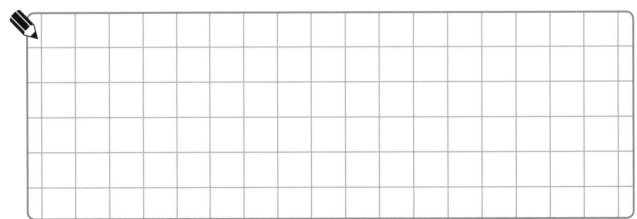

5 Match each shape to the correct description and name.

 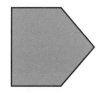  

| D | 5 | _____ | _____ | _____ | _____ | _____ |

A has perpendicular lines, but is not a quadrilateral.	**B** has one line of vertical symmetry, three acute angles and one pair of sides the same length.	**C** has two acute and two obtuse angles, and all sides are equal length.
D has one line of vertical symmetry and is not a quadrilateral.	**E** has two pairs of parallel lines and four pairs of perpendicular lines.	**F** has two pairs of sides the same length.
1 triangle	**2** rectangle	**3** pentagon
4 rhombus	**5** semi-circle	**6** kite

Reflect

Explain three different ways you can recognise a rectangle.

→ Textbook 3C p124

Recognising and describing 3D shapes

1 Name each shape.

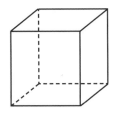 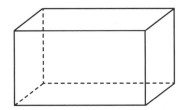 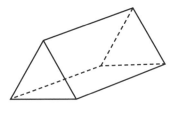

_____   _____   _____

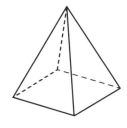 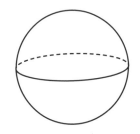 

_____   _____   _____

2 Write the number of vertices, faces and edges for each shape.

Shape				
Vertices				
Faces				
Edges				

3 Match each cuboid to its set of faces.

a)

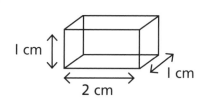

b)

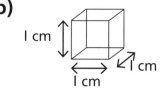

c)

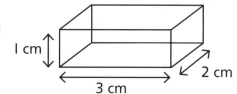

i)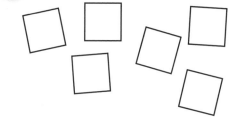

ii)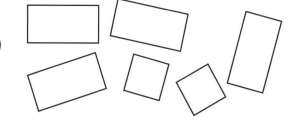

iii)

4 Write the letters for each shape in the correct parts of the table.

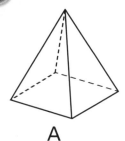   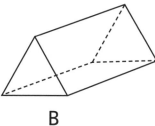   C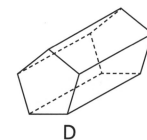

A   B   C   D

	Has more than one rectangular face	Has one rectangular face
Prism		
Not a prism		

5 Compare these two shapes.

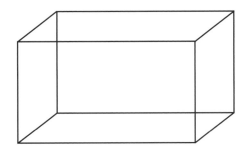 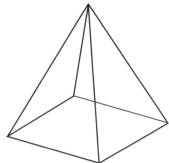

Use these words: parallel, perpendicular, faces, edges, symmetrical.

I noticed that …

both shapes have _____

_____

the cuboid has _____

_____

but the pyramid has _____

_____

Reflect

Write a checklist for recognising a cube.

 _____

 _____

_____

_____

Constructing 3D shapes

1 How many cubes are used to make each of these shapes?

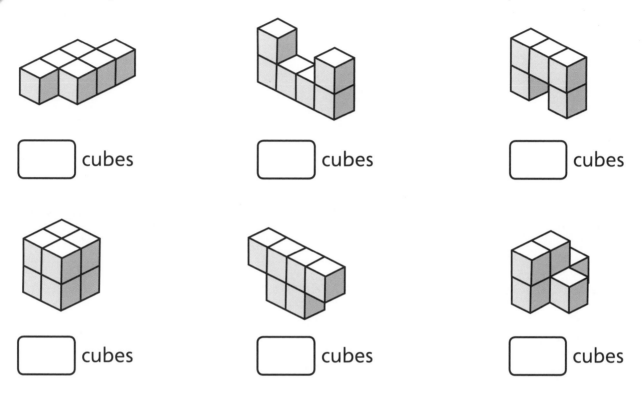

[ ] cubes   [ ] cubes   [ ] cubes

[ ] cubes   [ ] cubes   [ ] cubes

2 How many different cuboids has Reena made?

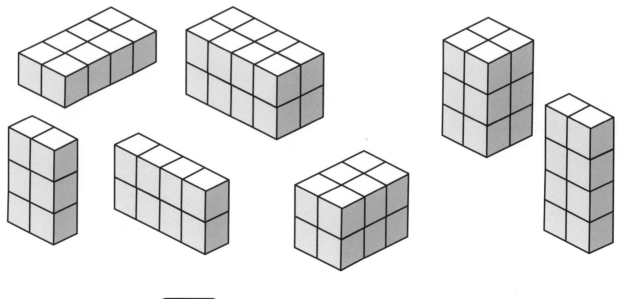

Reena has made [ ] different cuboids.

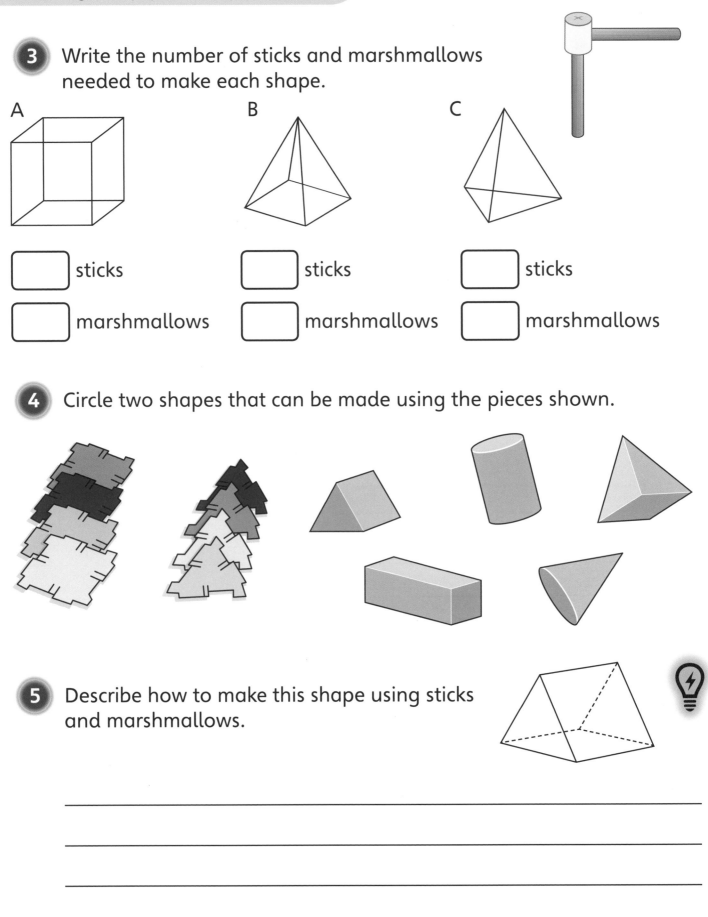

3 Write the number of sticks and marshmallows needed to make each shape.

A

B

C

[ ] sticks   [ ] sticks   [ ] sticks

[ ] marshmallows [ ] marshmallows [ ] marshmallows

4 Circle two shapes that can be made using the pieces shown.

5 Describe how to make this shape using sticks and marshmallows.

_____

_____

_____

_____

6 Explore the different numbers of sticks and marshmallows needed to make each of these prisms.

CHALLENGE

	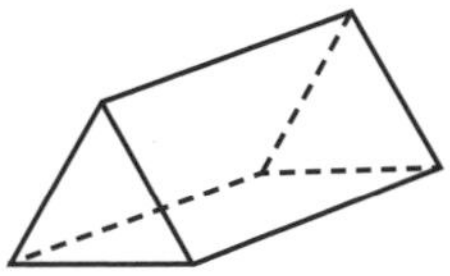	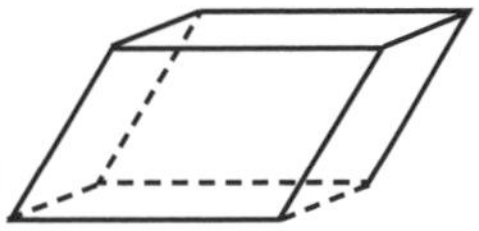	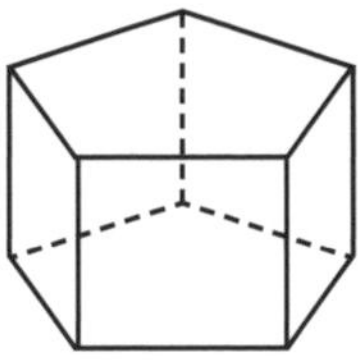	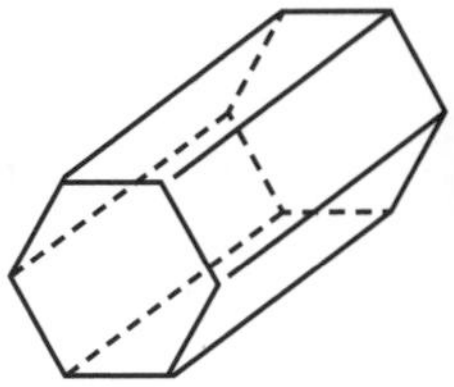
Sticks				
Marshmallows				

Explain any patterns you notice.

_____

_____

_____

_____

_____

Reflect

List three of the most important things you have learnt in this unit.

- _____
- _____
- _____
- _____

→ Textbook 3C p132

End of unit check

My journal

 a) Split the large square into these shapes.

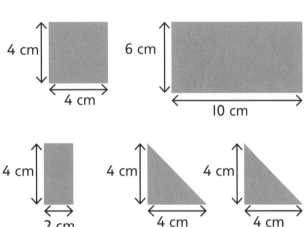

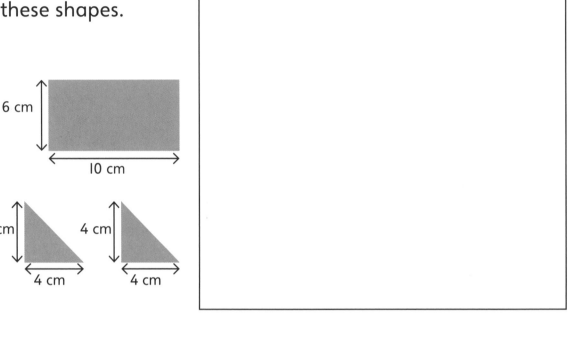

b) Describe how you made sure the shapes were accurate. Use some of the keywords below.

Keywords

vertical, horizontal, parallel, angle, right angle, measure

_____

_____

_____

2 On the grid below, draw and label:

a) a pair of parallel lines where the lines are **not** vertical or horizontal

b) a pair of perpendicular lines

c) a quadrilateral with at least two right angles that is **not** a square or a rectangle

d) a pentagon with just one right angle

a)

b)

c)

d)

Power check

How do you feel about your work in this unit?

Power play

Explore how to use cubes to make a 3D shape with no symmetry.

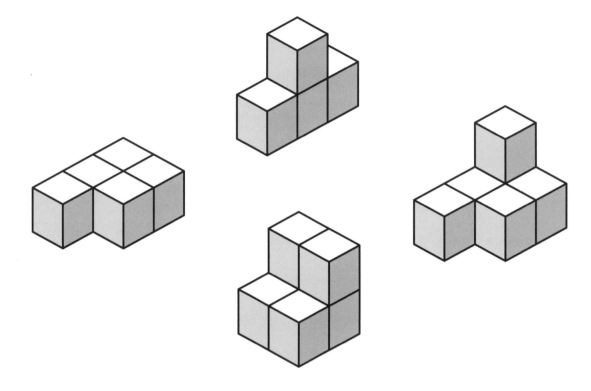

What is the fewest
number of cubes
you need?

Measuring mass ①

① Draw the pointer to the correct place on each measuring scale.

a)

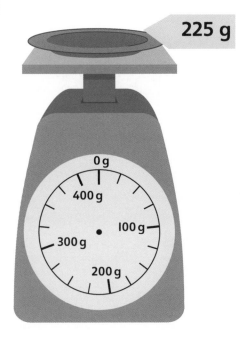

225 g

b)

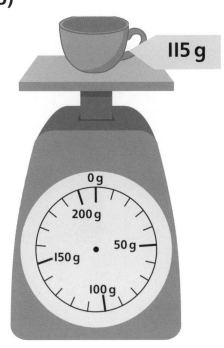

115 g

c)

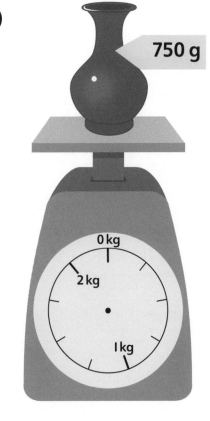

750 g

d)

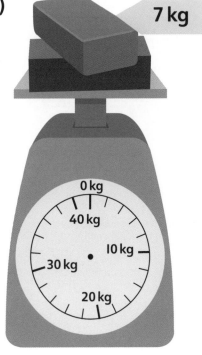

7 kg

2 Look at the two scales. There are no units marked.
Why could the second object weigh more than the first?

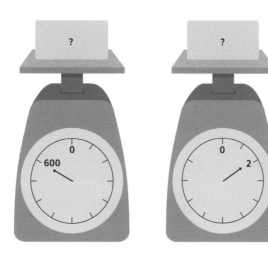

I will use my knowledge of grams and kilograms.

The second object could weigh more because

_____

_____

_____

_____

3 Andy thinks that the scale shows a mass of 250 g. Do you agree?

4 **a)** Name some objects that might have the following masses.

    1) 8 kg _____

    2) 180 g _____

    3) 28 g _____

b) Now write the name of each object above the correct number line.

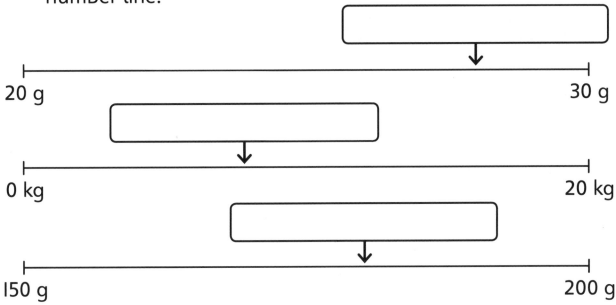

Reflect

Draw a number line that shows 200 g, 500 g and 600 g.

→ Textbook 3C p140

Measuring mass

1 Draw the pointer to the correct place on each measuring scale.

a)

b)

c)

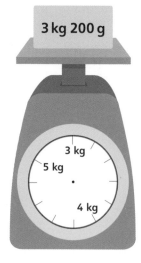

2 Match the amounts to the scale readings.

2 kg 100 g

2 kg 50 g

2 kg 125 g

3 Estimate the mass shown by each arrow.

a)
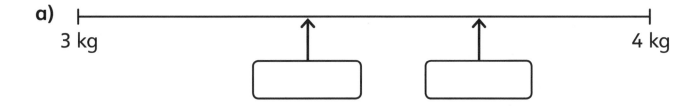

3 kg 4 kg

b)
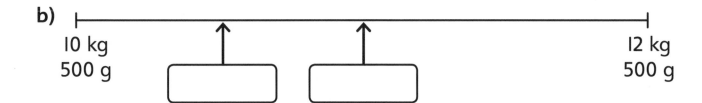

10 kg 500 g 12 kg 500 g

c)
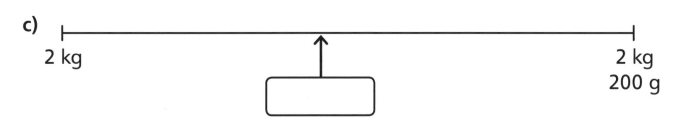

2 kg 2 kg 200 g

4 Tom measures the mass of a spade to the nearest kilogram. He finds that the spade has a mass of 9 kg. What could the mass of the spade actually be?

I wonder if there is more than one answer.

Reflect

Explain how to read a scale accurately when the pointer is between marked intervals.

Measuring mass ③

1 Complete the part-whole models.

a)

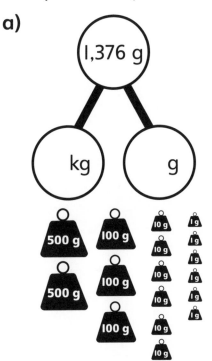

b)

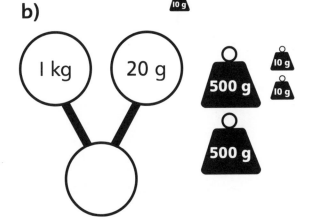

c)

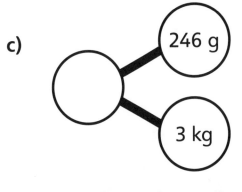

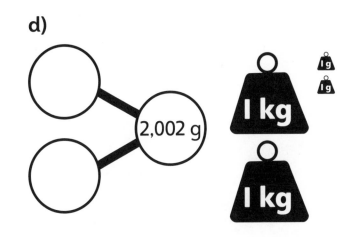

d)

2 Complete the table.

Mass in kilograms and grams	Mass in grams
1 kg 456 g	
	2,132 g
1 kg 88 g	
	654 g

107

3 Read the scales and write each mass in grams. Then write the mass in kilograms and grams.

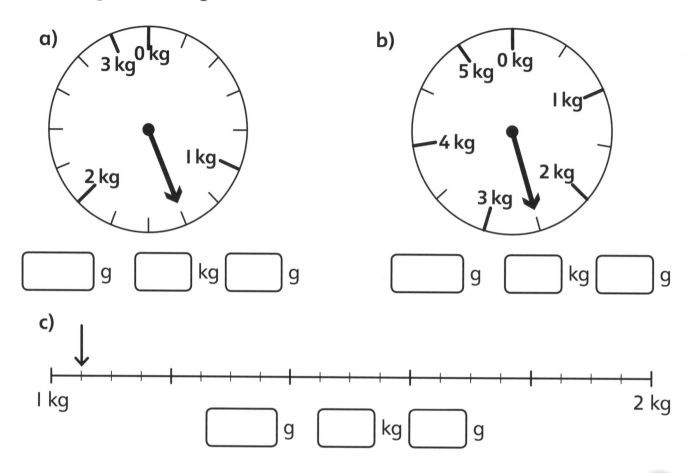

a)

☐ g   ☐ kg ☐ g

b)

☐ g   ☐ kg ☐ g

c)

1 kg   2 kg

☐ g   ☐ kg ☐ g

4 Is Lee correct? Explain why.

The sugar weighs 1,090 g.

Lee

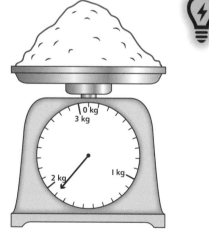

Lee is correct / incorrect because _____

_____

_____

5 How many different ways can you balance 2 kg 750 g using the weights? You can use the same weight more than once. Draw your answers below.

CHALLENGE

I will look carefully at the units first.

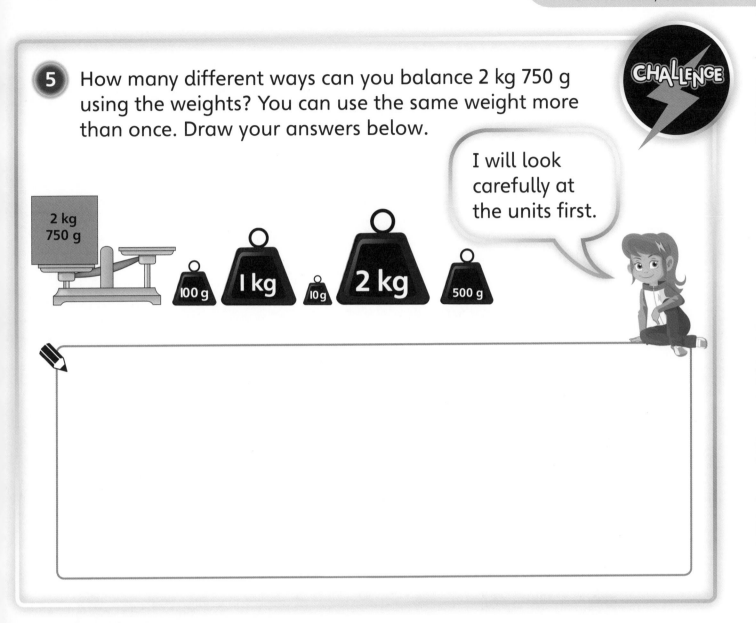

Reflect

Think of some real-life situations when you would need to write amounts in just grams and when you would need kilograms and grams.

→ Textbook 3C p148

Comparing masses

1 Use <, > and = to compare these amounts.

a) 1,321 g ◯ 1 kg 300 g

b) 1 kg 8 g ◯ 1,080 g

c) 2 kg 10 g ◯ 2,010 g

d) 983 g ◯ 0 kg 899 g

2 Circle the scale with the lightest weight of nuts on it.

3 Estimate the mass shown by where the arrow is pointing.

a)

I kg   2 kg

b)

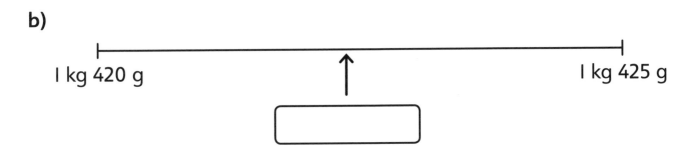

I kg 420 g   I kg 425 g

c)

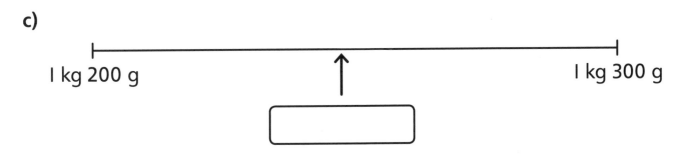

I kg 200 g   I kg 300 g

4 A is heavier than B. C is heavier than A. D is lighter than B.

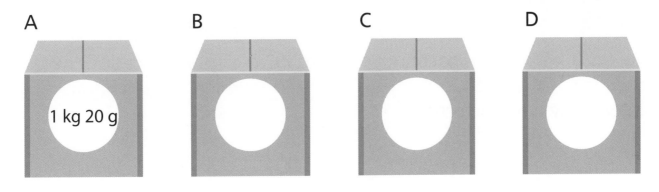

A   B   C   D

1 kg 20 g

What could the masses of B, C and D be?

B = [   ]   C = [   ]   D = [   ]

5 Order these amounts.

I know how to compare two amounts, so I can use my knowledge to compare more.

CHALLENGE

a) 1,540 g   1 kg 500 g   2 kg   1,999 g

lowest ⬚ ⬚ ⬚ ⬚ highest

b) 1,010 g   1 kg 100 g   1,110 g   1,001 g

lowest ⬚ ⬚ ⬚ ⬚ highest

c) 1,777 g   1 kg 707 g   1 kg 700 g   1,070 g

lowest ⬚ ⬚ ⬚ ⬚ highest

Reflect

Max has 1 kg 265 g of coconuts and 1 kg 157 g of plums. He says he only needs to look at the 10s of grams to find out which mass is bigger. Explain why he is incorrect.

_____

_____

_____

Adding and subtracting masses

1 Complete the number lines.

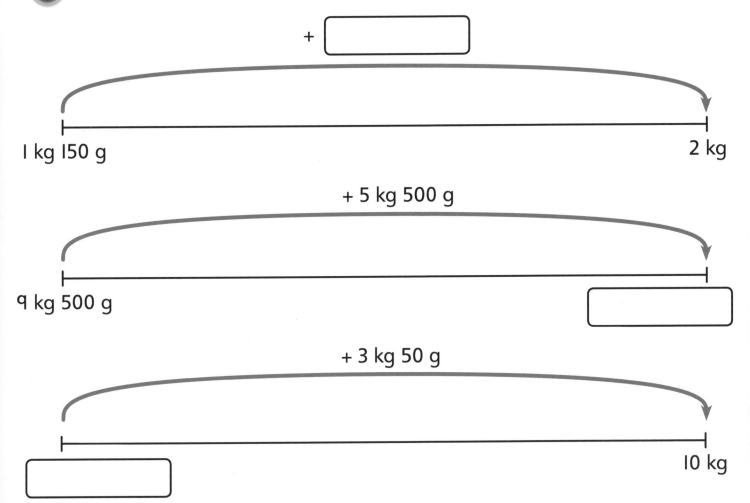

2 Complete the bar models.

1 kg 200 g	600 g

1 kg 100 g	

1 kg 300 g	
900 g	

1 kg 750 g	
	310 g

3 **a)** Alex has 1 kg 400 g of baking powder. She puts 1 kg 250 g back on the shelf. How much does she have left?

Alex has [   ] left.

b) Zac has 300 g of spices. How much more does he need if he wants to buy 1 kg 250 g altogether?

Zac needs [   ] more.

c) Zac buys 1 kg 300 g more flour than Alex. If the total amount they buy is 2,500 g, how much does Alex buy?

Alex buys [   ] of flour.

4 A question is solved with the calculation 1 kg 50 g − 250 g. Write a suitable story problem.

_____

_____

5 Complete the missing numbers.

a) 300 g + [　　　　　　] = 1 kg 200 g

b) [　　　　　　] + 1 kg 300 g = 1 kg 850 g

c) 1 kg 900 g − [　　　　　　] = 800 g

d) 1 kg 100 g − [　　　　　　] = 20 g

e) [　　　　　　] − 1 kg 310 g = 1 kg 400 g

I will check my answers using a different strategy.

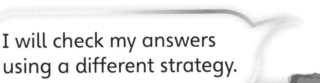

Reflect

Which methods did you learn about and how did you use them in this lesson?

I learnt that _____

_____

Now I can _____

_____

→ **Textbook 3C p156**

Problem solving – mass

1 **a)** Anwar starts with 320 g of sugar. He adds 150 g, 5 times.
Complete the number line to find the total amount.

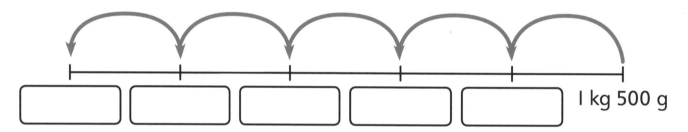

320 g

b) Eli starts with 1 kg 500 g of sugar. He takes away 250 g, 5 times.
Complete the number line to find out how much he has left.

1 kg 500 g

2 Work out the mass of nuts in this recipe.

450 g flour
650 g sugar
200 g butter
? nuts
Total mass: 1 kg 750 g

3 Amal had I kg 500 g of clay.

He used 400 g to make a vase and 550 g for a statue.

How much clay did Amal have left?

I kg 500 g

Amal had ☐ g of clay left.

4 Jamilla has 3 guinea pigs.

The youngest weighs 550 g and the oldest weighs 800 g. In total, all three weigh 2 kg.

How much does the middle guinea pig weigh?

The middle guinea pig weighs ☐ g.

5 What is the mass of the heart?

Do you remember what you did last time you came across a similar problem?

CHALLENGE

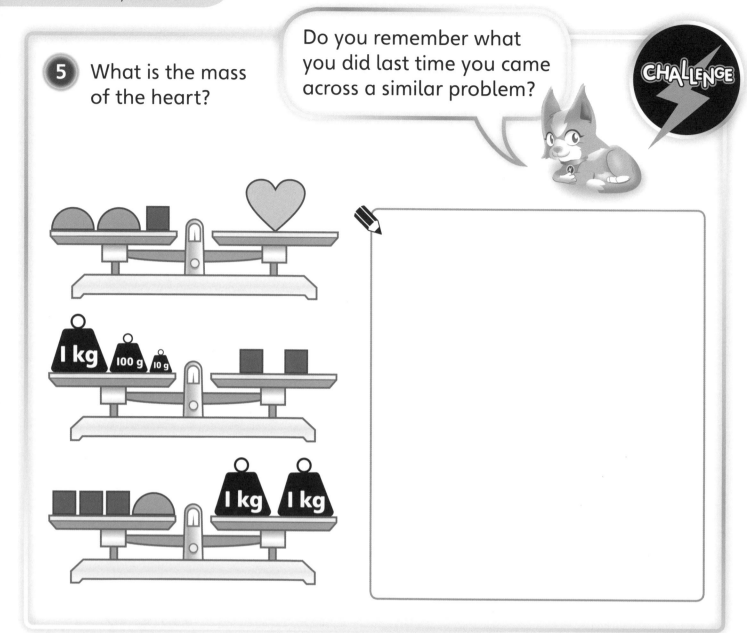

Reflect

The answer to a question is 2 kg 550 g. What could the question be?

End of unit check

My journal

I Explain how to calculate the mass of the melon.

Power check

How do you feel about your work in this unit?

Power play

Make up your own version of this game with a partner!

Play with a partner. Put your counters on START.

Roll a dice and move forwards the number shown.

Complete the task described at the top of the column you land in.

Get your partner to check your answer.

If you get the answer right, stay where you are.

If you get the answer wrong, move back a space!

Add 5 kg	Say the amount in kilograms and grams	Add 5 kg	Add 650 kg	Add 5 kg	Make up a word problem with this as the answer!	Subtract 110 g
START	1,400 g	225 g	25 g	1,350 g	1,999 g	302 g
2,000 g	1,000 g	900 g	950 g	820 g	1,820 g	1,500 g
1,600 g	410 g	1,100 g	500 g	1,110 g	110 g	1,001 g
1,750 g	1,800 g	1,500 g	990 g	1,050 g	1,005 g	1,501 g
2,010 g	640 g	1,150 g	1,080 g	1,300 g	1,710 g	664 g
END	1,700 g	890 g	510 g	1,660 g	300 g	115 g

Measuring capacity ①

① Record how much liquid there is in each container.

I wonder what each interval is worth.

a)

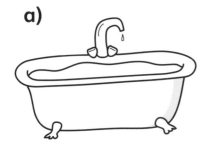

500 ml
400 ml
300 ml
200 ml
100 ml
0 ml

[ ] ml

b)

100 ml
50 ml
0 ml

[ ] ml

c)

1,000 ml
800 ml
600 ml
400 ml
200 ml
0 ml

[ ] ml

② Which measure would you use? Write millilitres or litres under each item.

a)

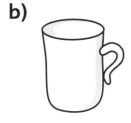

_____

c)

_____

e)

_____

b)

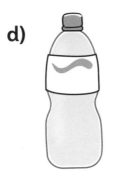

_____

d)

_____

3 Write the letters of each container in order from the least amount of liquid to the greatest amount.

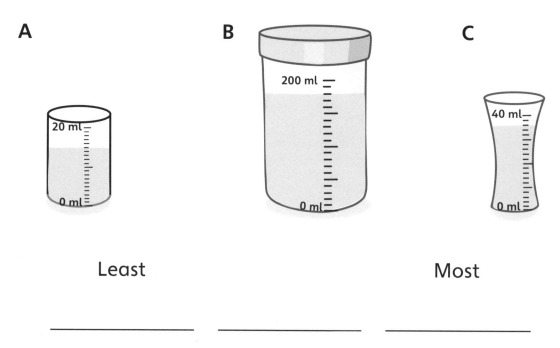

A

B

C

Least

Most

_____   _____   _____

4 Draw the arrow on each fuel gauge so that it points to 40 litres.

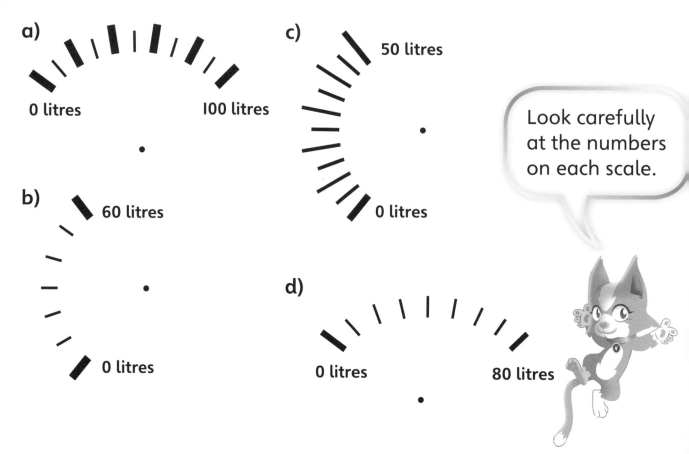

a)

0 litres

100 litres

b)

60 litres

0 litres

c)

50 litres

0 litres

d)

0 litres

80 litres

Look carefully at the numbers on each scale.

CHALLENGE

5 How can you divide the scales so that you can measure 100 ml?

Use a ruler.

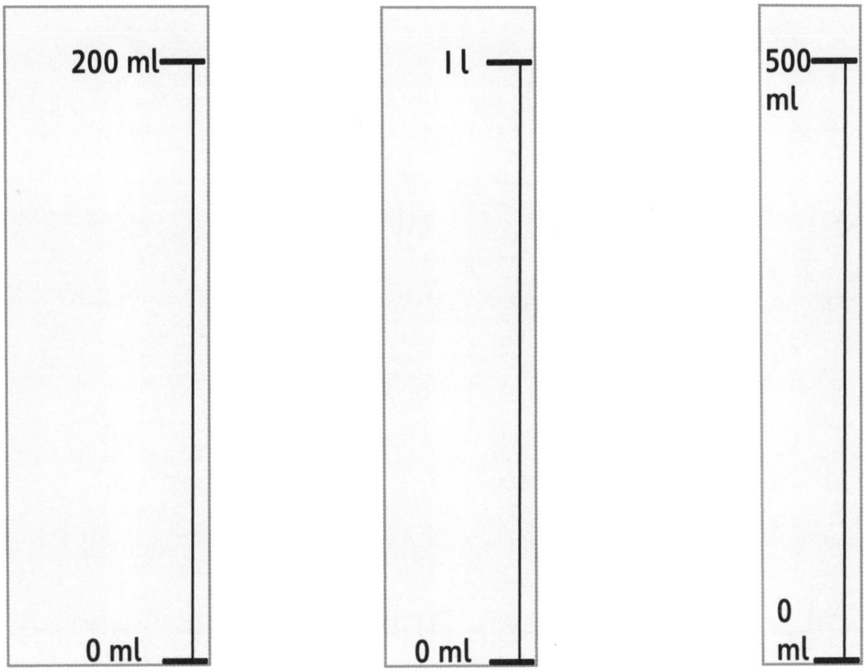

200 ml

0 ml

1 l

0 ml

500 ml

0 ml

I will need a ruler for this.

Reflect

To work out how much liquid is in a measuring jug, I need to _____

_____

_____

→ Textbook 3C p168

Measuring capacity ②

1 **a)** Write the amounts in l and ml.

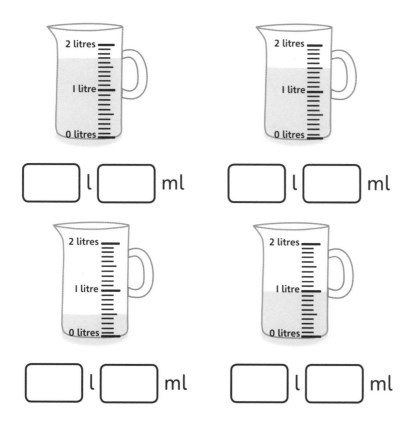

☐ l ☐ ml   ☐ l ☐ ml

☐ l ☐ ml   ☐ l ☐ ml

b) How much is in each jug?

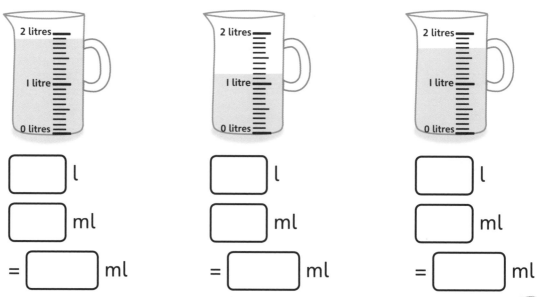

☐ l   ☐ l   ☐ l

☐ ml   ☐ ml   ☐ ml

= ☐ ml   = ☐ ml   = ☐ ml

I wonder if 1 l = 1,000 ml will
help me to answer this question.

2 Colour the correct amount of liquid in each measuring jug.

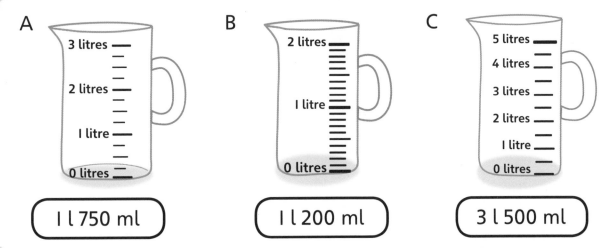

A

3 litres
2 litres
1 litre
0 litres

1 l 750 ml

B

2 litres
1 litre
0 litres

1 l 200 ml

C

5 litres
4 litres
3 litres
2 litres
1 litre
0 litres

3 l 500 ml

3 Draw the needle in the correct place on each fuel gauge.

A

0 l   1 l 2 l 3 l 4 l   5 l

3 l 750 ml

B

0 l   5 l

2 l 250 ml

4 The large jug was empty. Then one smaller full jug was tipped into it. Which smaller jug was used?

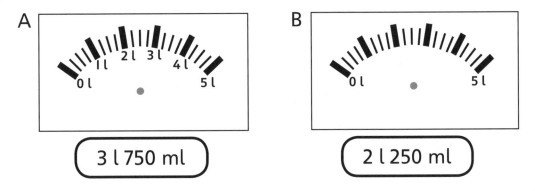

3 litres
0 litres

A
1,500 ml
1,000 ml
500 ml
0 ml

B
2,000 ml
1,500 ml
1,000 ml
500 ml
0 ml

C
2,500 ml
2,000 ml
1,500 ml
1,000 ml
500 ml
0 ml

> I think I need to work out how much is in the big jug first.

Jug [ ] was used.

5 Approximately how much is in the jug?

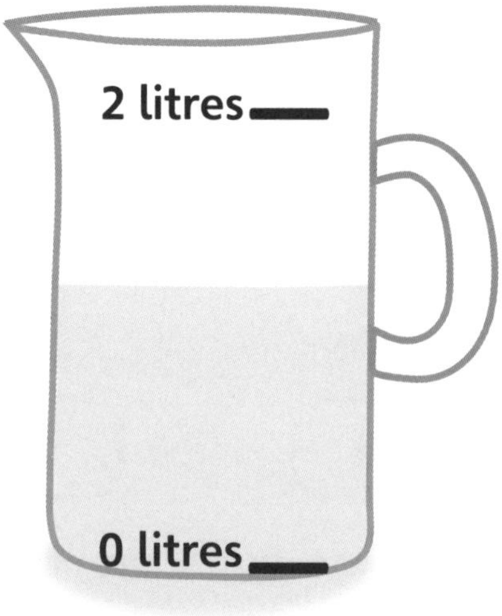

CHALLENGE

2 litres

0 litres

I think ⬚ l ⬚ ml is a good estimate because

_____

_____

_____

Reflect

Draw scales to show a litre split into 4 intervals and 5 intervals. Show the different labels for each.

Measuring capacity ③

1 **a)** Convert 1,100 ml into litres and millilitres.

1,100 ml = [   ] l and [   ] ml

b) Complete the bar model and the part-whole model to convert 2,300 ml into litres and millilitres.

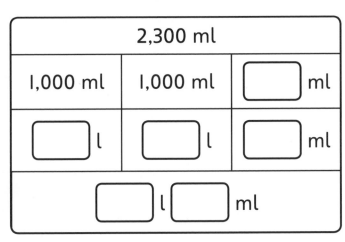

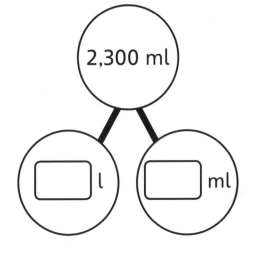

2,300 ml = [   ] l [   ] ml

2 Draw a model to convert

3 l 700 ml into millilitres.

3 l 700 ml = [   ] ml

3 How many millilitres are in each milk bottle?

 2 l 270 ml

 3 l 450 ml

a) 2 l 270 ml = [ ] ml   b) 3 l 450 ml = [ ] ml

4 Write the amounts shown in two different ways.

a) [ ] ml = [ ] l [ ] ml b) [ ] ml = [ ] l [ ] ml

 50 is half-way between 0 and 100. I can work out half-way between other 100s.

5 Show 1$\frac{1}{4}$ litres on the measuring cylinder. Write the same capacity in litres and millilitres in the boxes.

[ ] ml = [ ] l [ ] ml

6 Mark approximately where 2,250 ml is on the scale.

I will start by marking where 1 litre and 2 litres are.

Reflect

How would you convert a measurement in millilitres into a measurement in l and ml?

I would _____

_____

_____

_____

_____

_____

_____

→ Textbook 3C p176

Comparing capacities

1 Write >, < or = to compare the amounts.

a) 1 l 200 ml ◯ 2 l 100 ml

c) 500 ml ◯ $\frac{1}{2}$ l

b) 1 l ◯ 900 ml

d) 2 l 100 ml ◯ 1 l 999 ml

2 Write these amounts in order, from greatest to smallest.

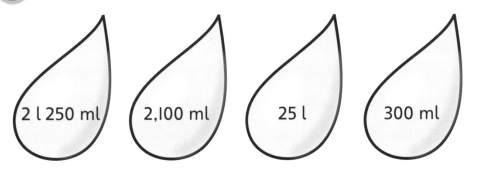

2 l 250 ml   2,100 ml   25 l   300 ml

I will need to check carefully. There are litres, millilitres and a mix of both litres and millilitres.

Greatest amount to smallest:

◻ ◻ ◻ ◻

3 Order the containers from greatest to smallest capacity.

A   B   C   D

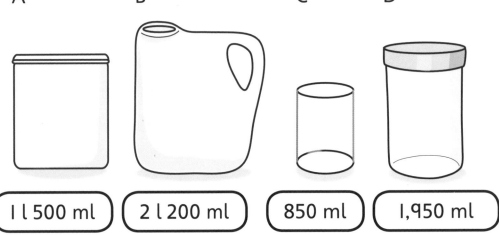

1 l 500 ml   2 l 200 ml   850 ml   1,950 ml

Greatest   Smallest

◻ ◻ ◻ ◻

I will use the fact 1,000 ml = 1 l to work out how many litres and millilitres D has.

4 Order the containers by capacity, from least to most.

A   B   C   D

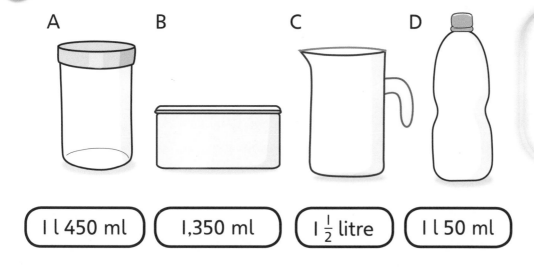

I need to think carefully about the difference between $\frac{1}{2}$ l and 50 ml.

(1 l 450 ml)   (1,350 ml)   (1 $\frac{1}{2}$ litre)   (1 l 50 ml)

Least   Most

☐ ☐ ☐ ☐

5 Look at the amounts shown by the arrows. Put them in order, from smallest to greatest amount.

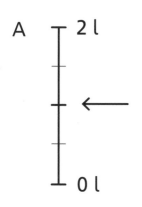

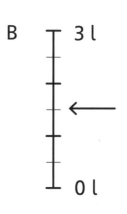

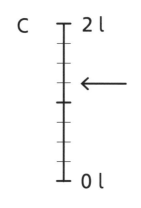

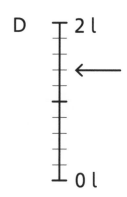

Smallest ☐ ml ☐ ml ☐ ml ☐ ml Greatest

6 Jessica needs a mixing bowl. It should hold less than $2\frac{1}{2}$ l, but more than $1\frac{1}{4}$ l. Which one should she choose?

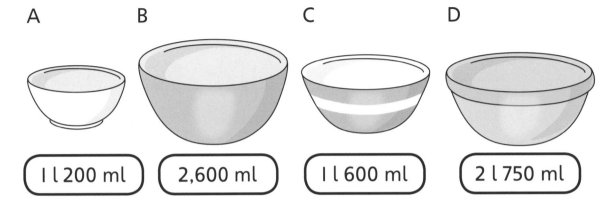

A   B   C   D

| 1 l 200 ml | 2,600 ml | 1 l 600 ml | 2 l 750 ml |

Jessica should choose bowl _____ .

7 Which container has more liquid in it?
Explain your reasoning.

CHALLENGE

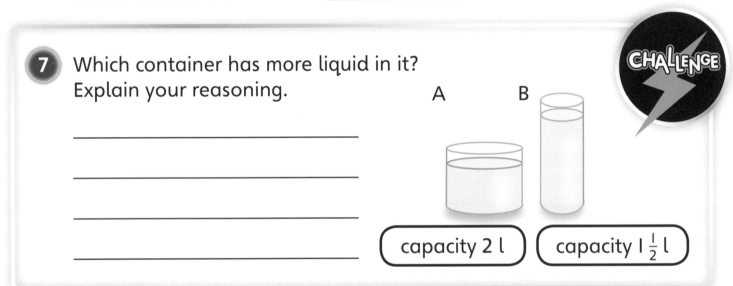

A   B

_____

_____

_____

_____

| capacity 2 l | capacity $1\frac{1}{2}$ l |

Reflect

Write the steps you need to take to order 2,400 ml, 3 l 500 ml and $2\frac{1}{2}$ l.

1 _____

2 _____

3 _____

Adding and subtracting capacities

1 **a)** What is the total of these two amounts?

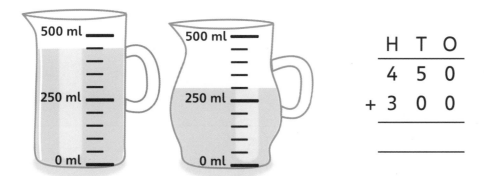

```
  H  T  O
  4  5  0
+ 3  0  0
─────────

```

The total of the two amounts is ☐ ml.

b) What is the total of these two amounts?

1 l 500 ml		500 ml
1 l	500 ml	500 ml
☐ l		

The total of the two amounts is ☐ l.

c) What is the total of 3 l 250 ml + 2 l 425 ml?

I will try adding the litres and millilitres separately.

133

2 The cup has been filled from the bottle. How much liquid is left in the bottle?

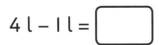

2 l   250 ml

There is ☐ l ☐ ml left in the bottle.

3 How much will be left in the large container?

4 l – 1 l = ☐

```
  H  T  O
  5  0  0   ml
– 1  5  0   ml
_____
```

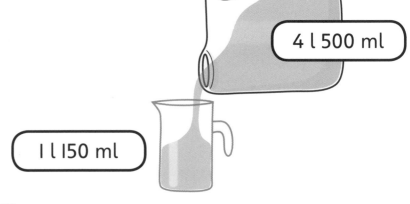

4 l 500 ml

1 l 150 ml

There will be ☐ l ☐ ml left in the large container.

4 James needs 3 l of water. He has two jugs with 750 ml in each. How much more water does he need?

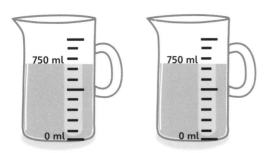

750 ml   750 ml

0 ml   0 ml

I wonder if a bar model or a number line would help.

James needs ☐ l ☐ ml more water.

5 The liquid in the three cylinders exactly fills the 2 l jug. How much is in cylinder C?

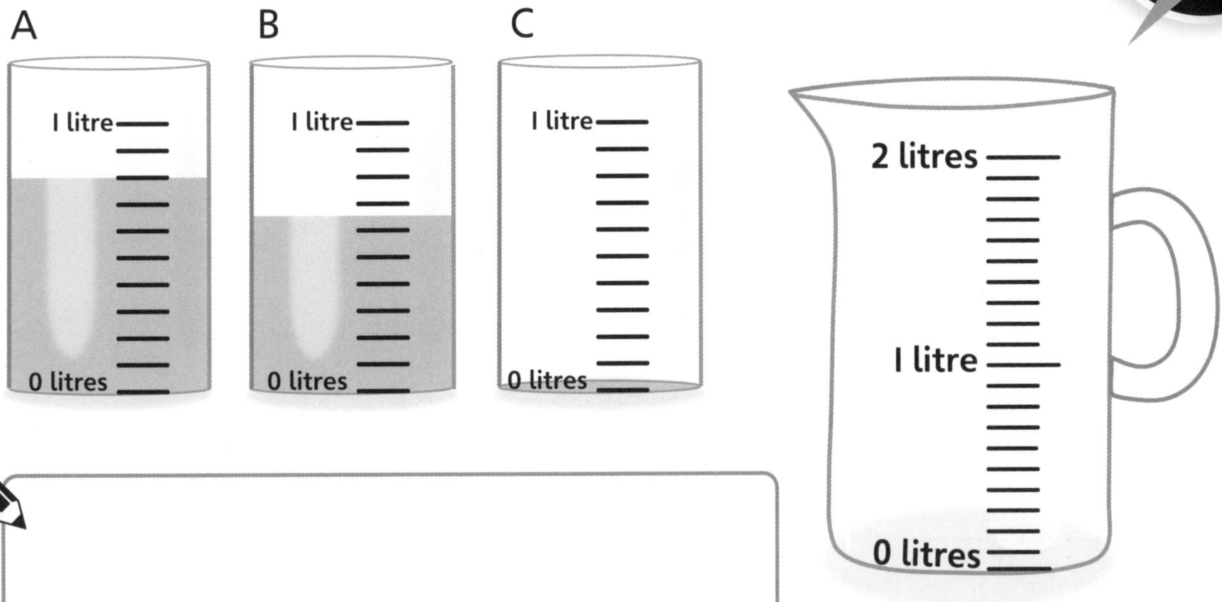

CHALLENGE

A

B

C

I litre

0 litres

I litre

0 litres

I litre

0 litres

2 litres

I litre

0 litres

There are ⬚ ml in cylinder C.

Reflect

Explain how to add together 2 l 800 ml and 1,250 ml.

→ **Textbook 3C p184**

Problem solving – capacity

1 Paolo bought 4 bottles of water. Each bottle contained 200 ml. How much water did he buy altogether?

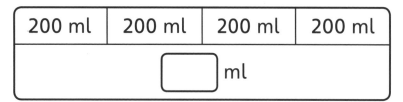

200 ml	200 ml	200 ml	200 ml
ml

Paolo bought [ ] ml of water altogether.

2 Maria has a 2 l bottle of water. She can fill 4 identical glasses. How much does each glass hold?

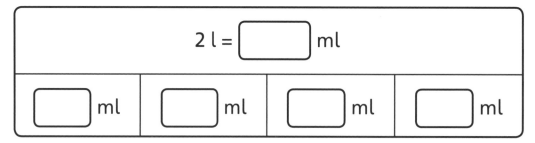

2 l = [ ] ml

| [ ] ml | [ ] ml | [ ] ml | [ ] ml |

Each glass holds [ ] ml of water.

3 Frederica puts 40 l of fuel in her car. She uses $\frac{1}{4}$ of the fuel. How much does she have left?

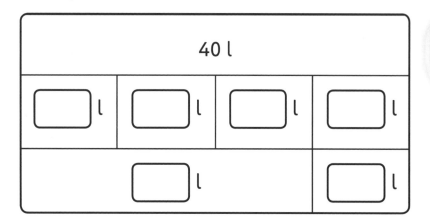

40 l

| [ ] l | [ ] l | [ ] l | [ ] l |
| [ ] l | | | [ ] l |

To find $\frac{1}{4}$ of a number, divide by 4.

Frederica has [ ] l of fuel left.

4 A cook uses $\frac{1}{2}$ litre plus three 250 ml cartons of milk.

How much milk is that in total?

250 ml	[ ] ml	[ ] ml	$\frac{1}{2}$ litre
[ ] ml			[ ] ml
[ ] ml			

The total is [ ] ml. This is [ ] l [ ] ml of milk in total.

5 Alfredo and Jen each like to drink 2 l of water a day. Alfredo drinks a 250 ml glass and Jen drinks a 200 ml glass. How many more glasses of water do Alfredo and Jen each need to drink today?

Alfredo needs to drink [ ] more glasses.

Jen needs to drink [ ] more glasses.

6 A chef needs 5 l of cream for his recipe. He has five cartons of cream with 500 ml in each. How much more cream does he need?

He needs [ ] l and [ ] ml more cream.

7 A tomato plant needs 500 ml of water a day. How much water will you need to water 5 plants for 3 days?

CHALLENGE

You will need [ ] l [ ] ml.

Reflect

Explain how you worked out the answer to a question that needed more than one calculation.

End of unit check

My journal

1 Convert these capacities.

a)

4 l				250 ml
⬚ ml	⬚ ml	⬚ ml	⬚ ml	250 ml
⬚ ml				

b)

2 ½ l		
⬚ ml	⬚ ml	500 ml
⬚ ml		

c)

3,750 ml			
⬚ ml	⬚ ml	⬚ ml	⬚ ml
⬚ l			⬚ ml

Power check

How do you feel about your work in this unit?

Power play

This is a game to play with your partner. You need a dice and two counters.

One of you will add on ml and the other will subtract ml.

To start the game place your counters at 2 l on the scale below.

Take turns to roll a dice.

Scores:
I: + or – **100** ml   2: + or – **200** ml   3: + or – **300** ml
4: + or – **400** ml   5: + or – **500** ml   6: + or – **600** ml

The first person to reach 4 l (adding) or 0 l (subtracting) wins.

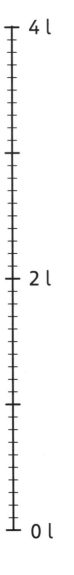

4 l

2 l

0 l

Can you make this game more challenging by drawing a different scale?

My power points

Colour the ☆ next to the topics you have done.

Colour the ☺ when you feel confident about the topic.

Unit 10

I can ...

☆ ☺ Show equivalent fractions using fraction strips

☆ ☺ Show equivalent fractions on a number line

☆ ☺ Find equivalent fractions

☆ ☺ Compare two fractions using fraction strips

☆ ☺ Order a set of fractions on a number line

☆ ☺ Add fractions with the same denominator

☆ ☺ Subtract two fractions with the same denominator

Unit 11

I can ...

☆ ☺ Understand about months in the year and days in the month

☆ ☺ Read analogue and digital clocks

☆ ☺ Talk about am and pm, and use a 12-hour clock and 24-hour clock

☆ ☺ Find and compare durations of time

☆ ☺ Find start and end times

☆ ☺ Measure time in seconds

Unit 12

I can ...

☆ ☺ Identify angles and turns

☆ ☺ Identify right angles in shapes

☆ ☺ Compare angles

☆ ☺ Identify and find horizontal and vertical symmetry

☆ ☺ Identify parallel lines and perpendicular lines

☆ ☺ Recognise and describe 2D shapes

☆ ☺ Recognise and describe 3D shapes

Unit 13

I can ...

☆ ☺ Measure mass in grams and kilograms

☆ ☺ Convert grams and kilograms

☆ ☺ Compare masses including mixed units

☆ ☺ Add and subtract masses

Unit 14

I can ...

☆ ☺ Measure capacity in millilitres and litres

☆ ☺ Convert millilitres and litres

☆ ☺ Compare capacities including mixed units

☆ ☺ Add and subtract capacities

Keep up the good work!

Notes

Notes